Man's Destiny

This is a profound and stimulating study of the entire span of life on earth, written by a leading scientist, Dr. George Gaylord Simpson, chairman of the Department of Geology and Paleontology at the American Museum of Natural History.

Dr. Simpson answers, simply and straightforwardly, the fundamental questions about the evolution of life and its meaning in terms of man's nature, ethical standards and destiny. He follows the rise and fall of the dynasties of life through the two billion years of the history of earth and explains clearly and concisely the modern views on the principles of evolution.

"This masterly book . . . should rank as one of the triumphs of science popularization of our time. The author, a leading paleontologist, has written the first adequate account for laymen of present day evolutionary thinking, avoiding technical jargon without sacrificing either clarity or the stamp of authority."—*The New Yorker*

Dr. Simpson was graduated from Yale in 1923 and received his Ph.D. from Yale in 1926. He is a member of the National Academy of Science, the American Philosophical Society, the American Academy of Arts and Science, the Society for the Study of Evolution, the Society of Vertebrate Paleontology and many others. He is the author of more than 350 articles and several books. The original edition of this book was published by Yale University Press.

Other MENTOR Books You Will Enjoy
35 cents each

THE MEANING
OF EVOLUTION

*A Special Revised
and Abridged Edition*

by

GEORGE GAYLORD SIMPSON

A MENTOR BOOK
Published by THE NEW AMERICAN LIBRARY

Published as a MENTOR BOOK By Arrangement with Yale University Press

FIRST PRINTING, OCTOBER, 1951
SECOND PRINTING, JULY, 1952

FOR ANNE

MENTOR BOOKS are published by The New American Library of World Literature, Inc. 501 Madison Avenue, New York 22, New York

PRINTED IN THE UNITED STATES OF AMERICA

Preface

The present book is an abridgment and revision of *"The Meaning of Evolution:* A Study of the History of Life and of its Significance for Man,"· published by Yale University Press, to which the reader is referred for more complete discussion of certain points than is possible in this shorter book. That book was an expansion of the twenty-fifth series of Terry Lectures, delivered by the author at Yale University. Thanks are due to the Dwight Harrington Terry Foundation and to Yale University Press for the opportunity to present *"The Meaning of Evolution"* to the public and now to present a shortened and somewhat altered version of it to a still wider audience.

In this version, Part I of the original book, constituting nine chapters on "The Course of Evolution," has been radically abridged. The nine chapters give some detail regarding geological time, the fossil record, and the factual reconstruction of the history of life. This presentation of evidence is now condensed to the barest summary in Chapter I of the present book, in order to leave space for emphasis, in a shorter presentation, on the interpretation and significance of evolution. The seven chapters of Part II, "The Interpretation of Evolution," and the four chapters of Part III, "Evolution, Humanity, and Ethics," from *"The Meaning of Evolution"* are here presented without noteworthy abridgment. Some passages have been slightly changed, but the discussion and conclusions remain essentially as first written.

Thanks are again due to Drs. E. H. Colbert, N. D. Newell, A. Roe, and B. Schaeffer, who read and criticized the manuscript of the earlier, full version, and to J. C. Germann and N. Altshuler, who prepared the illustrations. Although it is not practical to list all their names, I now also wish to add thanks to the many authorities in various fields who have discussed *"The Meaning of Evolution"* with me since its publication, and also to reviewers who wrote constructive criticisms of that work.

New York, N. Y.   G. G. S.
December 10, 1950

Illustrations

Contents

Prologue

MOST OF what follows was written at Los Pinavetes, on the slope of San Pedro Mountain in northern New Mexico. The closing passages were written in Hollywood, California.

Outside my study window at Los Pinavetes rises a forest of stately and ancient ponderosa pines. There is a stream bordered by alders, willows, and mountain cottonwoods. Near by is an aspen grove, where trembling leaves have turned from green to flashing yellow and finally have fallen, as this writing has progressed and as another yearly cycle of life has passed from summer toward winter. In the interspersed glades and fields the wild rose thickets have developed their gorgeous hips and their leaves have turned crimson. A hundred other sorts of flowers have bloomed and gone, scattering seeds which lie waiting to repeat the miracle in another year, as they have for so many ages past.

Animal life, no less than vegetation, is abundant and evident here. By night a bear wanders by and mule deer track the mountain. These are timid folk who know, somehow, that they are marked as prey by man. Not so the many members of the squirrel family, unafraid and given to fits of chattering anger at the intruder: chipmunks, tufted-eared pine squirrels, side-striped ground squirrels, drab but bright-eyed prairie dogs, and the rest. Pack rats, clean and attractive, unlike their distant kin who have given rats a bad name, are busily preparing a winter home in the wood pile. Birds have become less abundant as the weather grew colder, but even after heavy frosts jays and woodpeckers are much in evidence and bands of juncos move through from breeding grounds above to winter range below. Trout swim in the stream and water striders skitter over its surface in the pools. There are a thousand or many thousands of other forms of life, from the eagle far up in the sky to invisibly microscopic organisms deep in the soil.

The landscape is literally packed with life. It is as full of living substance as it well could be.

In Hollywood, too, evidence of life is everywhere. Two-legged mammals jam the streets and all around them rise their strange constructions. The very hills are torn down for their passage and even the plants and animals are theirs.

Los Pinavetes and Hollywood are both parts of nature and

both bear testimony to the wonder of life. In the mountain forest is a sample of the beautiful and intricate relationships wrought by blind forces from the matrix of life. Within this matrix has arisen one animal, man, who works no longer blindly, often no longer beautifully, but still with fearful intricacy to make a Hollywood.

How has this all come about? Everyone knows that the city has a history. The general outlines, at least, are familiar: the Indians, the early white explorers, the missions, the Spanish town, the growth of the gaudy American metropolis. Changes are still visibly going on and the city is not the same for years or even for months in succession. The forest and its denizens have a history, too, no less than the city. It covers many millions of years as against the few centuries of the city's history. In fact the two are parts of the same larger history, the history of life. The brief history of the city arises out of the long history of the beasts of the forests and the plains and is the surprising culmination of this.

There are many ways of studying the history of life. The geneticist, raising tiny fruit flies in bottles, and the well driller, piercing thousands of feet of the earth's crust in search of oil, are both contributing to this study. One way of pursuing the study, the most direct way and the one around which all other contributions need to be organized to articulate the whole history, is that of the paleontologist. In his most immediate and narrow occupation, the paleontologist is a student of fossils, the preserved remains of ancient life. He seeks these in the rocks throughout all the lands of the earth, takes them to his laboratory, cleans them for study, compares them with each other, identifies and names their kinds, determines their ages, and finally sets up their associations and historical sequences. As with any other sort of worker, the paleontologist's day-by-day attention is mostly focused on the concrete and more or less routine details of the job in hand rather than on the broad whole of which this job is a small part.

When he does turn to these broader aspects, the paleontologist becomes not merely a student of fossils but a historian of life. The historian of life takes not only knowledge of fossils but also a tremendous array of pertinent facts from other fields of earth sciences and of life sciences and weaves them all into an integral interpretation of what the world of life is like and how it came to be so. Finally, he is bound to reflect still more deeply and to face the riddles of the meaning and nature of life and of man as well as problems of human values and conduct. The history of life certainly bears directly on all these riddles and problems, and realization of its own value demands investigation of this bearing.

This book is an attempt by one historian of life to convey an understanding of the forces acting on and through life and to interpret the history in terms significant to us all as humans. The whole emphasis is on these things: the principles of evolution and the human meaning of evolution. No space is devoted to proofs that evolution has, in fact, occurred. Such proofs are not only ample but also overwhelming. They are completely convincing to all who have studied them with reasonably open minds. Of course no amount of proof can convince those who simply do not want to know or to accept the truth. Such wishful thinkers cannot be persuaded by repetition, and those who do really want to know the truth already know the evidence or can readily find it in earlier works. Here the factual truth of evolution is taken as established and the enquiry goes on from there.

It is one thing to know that evolution has occurred, and quite another thing to explain how and why it has occurred. In the how and the why are the problems that are still under enquiry and that still occupy the attention of students all over the world. The present status of these studies and consideration of their meaning are, then, the important subjects for a modern introduction to evolution. The general plan of the present enquiry is to attempt to answer three questions:

What has happened in the course of the evolution of life?

How has this been brought about?

What meaning has this in terms of the nature of man, his values and ethical standards, and his possible destiny?

Discussion of the first question is here brief, confined to Chapter 1, although it is longer in the book on which this is based. The second question is covered in Chapters 2-8, and the third in Chapters 9-12.

Tremendous questions, these! To think that complete or final answers have been provided would require a measure of conceit impossible to anyone who has spent much time watching the play of life at Los Pinavetes, or even in Hollywood where conceit blossoms more easily. It is only possible to say that some progress toward comprehension has been made, to attest that the discussion is written in the spirit of loyalty to the truth and devotion to human welfare, and to hope that it will be read in the same spirit.

1. The Course of Evolution

THE MEANING of human life and the destiny of man cannot be separated from the meaning and destiny of life in general. "What is man?" is a special case of "What is life?" The extent to which we can hope to understand ourselves and to plan our future depends in some measure on our ability to read the riddles of the past. The present, for all its awesome importance to us who chance to dwell in it, is only a random point in the long flow of time. Life is one and continuous in space and in time. The processes of life can be adequately displayed only in the course of life throughout the long ages of its existence.

How old is life? We do not know, but we have some interesting clues. Aside from fantastic fiction, life can be no older than the earth. Measurements of the results of radioactivity in certain minerals have established that some rocks in the earth's crust are about 2,000,000,000 years old. There is evidence that even these astonishingly ancient rocks were formed long after the planet earth came into existence. The whole age of the earth is probably on the order of 3,000,000,000 years. That we judge to be the *possible* span of life on the earth, although a billion years or more may have passed after the earth was formed and before life arose.

How did life arise? Again, the honest answer is that we do not know but that we have some good clues. This ultimate mystery is more and more nearly approached by recent studies on the chemical activity of living particles, of viruses and of genes, the submicroscopic determiners of heredity and growth. The most fundamental properties of life are reproduction and change (or mutation). Particles with these properties would be, in essence, alive, and from them all more complex forms of life could readily arise. Current studies suggest that it would be no miracle, nor even a great statistical improbability, if living molecules appeared spontaneously under special conditions of surface waters rich in the carbon compounds that are the food and substance of life. And the occurrence of such waters at early stages of the planet's evolution is more probable than not. This is not to say that the origin of life was by chance or by supernatural intervention, but that it was in accordance with the grand, eternal physical laws of the universe. It need not have been miraculous, except as the existence of the physical universe may be considered a miracle.

Fossils, primary documents of the historians of life, can tell us nothing of the very earliest stages. Truly primeval life was tiny, fragile, soft-bodied, without resistant parts that can have endured such long burial in rocks heated and cooled, deep-sunk and upflung in the slow down-warpings and upheavals of the planet's crust. The oldest fossils surely recognized are simple water plants, algae, primitive enough, to be sure, and yet already several strides along the road of evolution. Their age is at least 1,000,000,000 years, perhaps more. Even after these first fossils, a tremendous time elapsed before life became highly varied or began to leave a fairly good and continuous fossil record. Evolution is a cumulative process and in it, as usual in such processes, there is an effect of acceleration. Early stages were aeon-long and slow almost beyond imagination. They built a basis on which, finally, more rapid evolution occurred.

One of the episodes of rapid evolution, and apparently the

TABLE 1
The Geologic Time Scale

Eras	Periods or Epochs	Approximate time since beginning, in millions of years
Cenozoic	RECENT	[About 20,000 years]
	PLEISTOCENE	1
	PLIOCENE	12
	MIOCENE	28
	OLIGOCENE	39
	EOCENE	58
	PALEOCENE	75
Mesozoic	CRETACEOUS	135
	JURASSIC	165
	TRIASSIC	205
Paleozoic	PERMIAN	230
	PENNSYLVANIAN	255
	MISSISSIPPIAN	280
	DEVONIAN	325
	SILURIAN	360
	ORDOVICIAN	425
	CAMBRIAN	505
Pre-Cambrian		[Beginning unknown; on the order of 3,000 million years]

most fundamental of all, occurred some 500,000,000 years or more ago, around the beginning of the Cambrian period of the geologists. At this point it is best to introduce the geologic time scale, by which the sequence and relative timing of events in the history of life are most readily dated, a sort of chronological shorthand convenient both for writer and for reader. As much of this scale as is needed for present purposes is given in Table 1.

At the beginning of the Cambrian, fossils became abundant, and their basic diversity increased rapidly through the Cambrian and the following period, the Ordovician. "Rapidly" must, to be sure, be considered relatively in this connection. The length of time involved was on the order of 100 to 150 million years, which is no short span even to a geologist. Yet it is only about a tenth of the length of the long pre-Cambrian preliminaries, and the evolutionary divergence of the organisms now appearing in the fossil record is really very profound and fundamental. Indeed during the Cambrian and Ordovician all the really important and really basic types of animal structure appear in the fossil record, although each was at first represented by relatively few and extremely primitive forms.

Most zoologists classify animals into about twenty major groups, called phyla (singular: phylum), each representing a fundamental anatomical plan. Some students recognize more than twenty phyla and some fewer, but the differences of opinion relate almost entirely to a small number of peculiar, soft-bodied living animals of uncertain origin, of no real importance in the modern fauna and practically without fossil records. Animals of real importance today or in the history of life may all be referred to only fifteen basic phyla. Five of these are collectively called "worms" and have poor fossil records. The other ten have, by and large, good fossil records and their histories since the Cambrian or Ordovician can be followed satisfactorily in broad outline, although it hardly needs saying that innumerable details need to be filled in.

The most important, broadest groups of animals in the history of life are as follows:[1]

1. Protozoa. These animals have no differentiation of their substance into separate cells, each individual consisting of a single mass of protoplasm analogous to one cell of higher animals, all of which are many-celled or metazoan. The relatively simple protozoan structure can function only in very small animals and most of them are microscopic. Among the many sorts of protozoans, the Foraminifera, secreting tiny limy supports or skeletons, are particularly abundant as fossils.

2. Porifera. These are the sponges. They are many-celled and some of the cells have differentiated functions, but they

[1] For more detailed descriptions and pictures of the highly diverse members of these phyla see B. Buchsbaum, *Animals without Backbones* (Rev. ed., Chicago, University of Chicago Press, 1948) and A. S. Romer, *Man and the Vertebrates* (3rd ed., Chicago, University of Chicago Press, 1941).

are not clearly arranged in definite layers or well divided into separate sorts of tissues. Many sponges have had internal supports which have left a long, although not a particularly continuous or impressive, fossil record.

3. Coelenterata. This is a large and highly varied phylum of aquatic, mostly marine, animals with the cells differentiated into two distinct tissue layers. The most familiar coelenterates, the corals, have left one of the best known fossil records.

4. Graptolithina. This is an extinct group of puzzling nature which probably does not merit recognition as a truly basic phylum. The trouble is that the preserved parts leave doubt as to which phylum should contain them. They are listed because they have left a rich fossil record and were evidently important denizens of the Paleozoic seas.

5.-9. Platyhelminthes. Nemertinea. Nemathelminthes. Trochelminthes. Annelida. These are mainly "worms" in popular conception, but their basic anatomical characters are so varied that separation into five phyla is warranted. Collectively, the "worms" are now extremely important in the economy of nature, but they are mostly small, soft-bodied forms and their fossil record is poor.

Fig. 1. Examples of the most important basic types, phyla, of animals. All the phyla include large numbers of extremely diverse animals many of which look radically different from these examples. For characterizations of each group see the text. The specimens are drawn to different scales.

10. Bryozoa. These are colonial, aquatic, mostly marine forms sometimes called "moss animals." They resemble some corals, but are more complex in having three, rather than two, primary tissue layers and a body cavity (coelom) in the middle layer. The colonies secrete skeletal supports which are easily fossilized and have given this group an unusually good fossil record.

11. Brachiopoda. These forms, the marine lamp shells, resemble clams in having two external shells. Unlike clams, however, each shell is usually symmetrical around a midline, and the internal anatomy is quite different from clams. Like all shells, they fossilize easily and have left an excellent historical record.

12. Echinodermata. This is an unusually varied phylum, including such forms as starfishes, sea urchins, and sea lilies. The tissue and organ differentiation is of advanced type. There is an underlying bilateral symmetry, but this is usually obscured by a secondary, five-rayed, radial symmetry. A complex skeleton of limy plates develops in the middle tissue layer and has resulted in a long and rich fossil record.

13. Mollusca. This is the most dominant and successful of the mainly aquatic phyla at present and through much of the history of life. Representatives include clams, snails, octopuses, and others. The fossil record is outstanding, probably better than for any other phylum.

14. Arthropoda. In sheer weight of numbers, this is the most successful of all the phyla, for it includes the insects, now several times more varied than all other animals put together. Other representatives are crabs, scorpions, spiders, and the extinct trilobites. Characteristics include a jointed body with legs and with a hard outer coating. The fossil record is good for some groups but it is deficient indication of the probable abundance of others, especially of the insects in later geologic times.

15. Chordata. Like some other advanced phyla, the chordates have complex tissue and organ differentiation and bilateral symmetry, to which they add basic mobility promoted by an internal longitudinal rod, jointed except in the most backward types. The jointed-backbone forms, comprising the bulk of the phylum, are the Vertebrata or vertebrates. Vertebrates include "fishes" (really four different aquatic groups), amphibians, reptiles, birds, and mammals. To us, they are the most interesting of animals because they include ourselves and the most familiar and conspicuous domestic and wild animals. The fossil record is generally good and is justifiably emphasized because of its special interest and application to man.

In figure 2 the relative variety of these major phyla today and the extent of their fossil records are shown. This is a picture, in broad strokes, of what is *known* of the history of life for the last 500,000,000 years. The notorious incompleteness of the fossil record, and the less publicized shortcomings of students of that record, keep the diagram from representing exactly the picture of life as it really existed. Yet the imperfections could be exaggerated, and it may fairly be claimed that this is strongly suggestive, at least, of the general course of events.

Duration and Diversity of the principal groups of animals (Based mainly on counts of genera and higher groups)

Fig. 2. The broad outlines of the historical record of life. In the lower figure the phyla of animals are represented by vertical bands or pathways the widths of which are proportional to the *known* variety (especially in terms of genera) of the phylum in each of the geological periods since the pre-Cambrian. The upper figure represents the approximate variety (in species) of each at the present time.

Several striking facts fundamental for the history of life appear in this diagram. First, all the phyla are of great antiquity. All date from the Cambrian or Ordovician. (Remember, however, that this does not mean that they all appeared suddenly or at the same time except in a very loose sense; Cambrian and Ordovician cover at least 100,000,000 years.) Since sometime in the Ordovician, around 400,000,000 years ago, no new *major* type of animal has appeared on earth. It would appear that the fundamental possibilities of animal structure had then all been developed, although truly profound changes and progressive developments were yet to occur within each type. The profundity of such changes is exemplified by the difference between a jawless "fish" (such as a lamprey) and man—both vertebrates, but how importantly different!

Note, second, that none of the basic types has become extinct. (The graptolites are only an apparent exception; it has been noted that it is improbable that they merit rank as a truly basic type.) Of the lesser types within phyla many, indeed most, have become extinct, but the major grades of organization persist. This extraordinary fact bothered Sigmund Freud, who could not see why all ancient forms have not yielded to a death wish, and it has bothered some others who feel that progressive evolution should imply constant replacement of all lower forms by higher. The explanation is really quite simple. In the filling of the earth with life, some broad spaces were filled first, filled well and adequately, leaving neither reason nor possibility for refilling by types of later development. A protozoan, because ancient and relatively simple, is not therefore an imperfect type destined for replacement within its own sphere. It is a fully adequate answer to the problems of life in that particular sphere. The sphere persists, and so do the protozoans. Other phyla represent, not advances over the protozoans for life as protozoans live it, but the development of other possibilities, other ways of life, and filling of other spheres in the economy of nature. There has, indeed, been replacement within given ways of life and expansion within types to more varied ways of life. Therefore new types of protozoans, or of vertebrates, have arisen and some have replaced earlier types, but the fundamental patterns of the phyla continue without extinction or replacement.

The third major generalization reflected in the diagram of figure 2 is that on the whole life has tended to increase in variety. The usual pattern for any phylum, or for life as a whole, is to appear in relatively few forms and later to become vastly more diversified. The pattern is quite irregular in many cases. Some phyla, like the sponges (Porifera), have expanded slowly and in no spectacular way. The Bryozoa expanded first with unusual rapidity, then declined, then expanded again. The chordates have fluctuated, with three fairly distinct expansions, each greater than the last. Marine animals as a whole lost ground, became less varied, around the Permian and Triassic when there was a great crisis for life in the seas. There is, nevertheless, an unmistakable general tendency for life to become more varied in the course of its history.

How this increase in variety has come about and what it

means are best seen within the histories of separate phyla, and
the vertebrates (in the Chordata) provide the best analyzed
and most interesting example. Their history is summarized in
figure 3. There are eight distinct types, classes in technical
classification, of vertebrates. The first four are primarily
aquatic and are usually lumped popularly as fishes: the jawless fishes (Agnatha, with lampreys and hagfishes as living
examples), the placoderms (Placodermi, no living examples),
the cartilage fishes (Chondrichthyes, including sharks and
rays among others), and the bony fishes (Osteichthyes, with
trout, perch, cod, herrings, and a whole host of others—most
of the fishes familiar to us today). The other four classes are
primarily terrestrial and are more commonly distinguished:
amphibians, reptiles, birds, and mammals, or Amphibia, Reptilia, Aves, and Mammalia in technical nomenclature.

Fig. 3. The broad outlines of the historical record of the vertebrates. For each vertebrate class the width of the pathway is proportional to its known variety in each of the geological periods in
which it lived.

These classes, too, as broad structural types subordinate
only to those of the phyla, have tended to persist. Only one of
the eight (Placodermi) is extinct. Yet most of them, five of
the eight, are less varied now than they were relatively early
in their histories and indeed only two, the bony fishes and the
birds, may now be at their peak. Among the vertebrates there
has been a succession from lower (or at least earlier) to higher (or later), and partial replacement of an ancestral by a
descendant type is common. In the aquatic habitat, the bony
fishes, among the last to arise, have replaced most other types.
The reptiles replaced most sorts of amphibians and most reptiles were in turn replaced by mammals and, to lesser extent,
by birds. Birds and mammals have hardly any tendency to

replace each other, for their ways of life are too radically different. Nor is there any strong tendency for birds and mammals to replace fishes, in spite of the fact that fishes are much older, because, again, the ways of life have little overlap.

Thus the net total expansion of the chordates, seen in figure 2, does not result from uniform expansion within the phylum, but from a complex sequence of origins of new types, some replacing older types and some expanding into quite new spheres of existence.

The same sorts of events have occurred within each class, and here may be seen still more clearly how a new type, once it has originated, tends to spread and to become diversified in adaptation to a variety of environmental conditions and of ways of life. This process is known as "adaptive radiation" and is particularly well shown by the reptiles, living and extinct. As shown in figure 4, the reptiles started with primitive, four-footed, long-tailed forms. From these, in different lines, arose immensely diverse reptiles: paddle-swimmers like the plesiosaurs; fish-like swimmers such as the ichthyosaurs; legless crawlers like the snakes; fliers, the pterodactyls; armored tanks like the turtles, and many others. The mammals are also an outcome of the reptilian radiation, but they represent an adaptation so potent and so superior in most spheres available to land-dwellers that they radiated in their turn on a grand scale and eventually largely replaced the reptiles.

Even more limited groups of reptiles, such as the dinosaurs, have diversified by adaptive radiation in a striking way, although with far less scope than for reptiles as a whole. Something of the diversity arising at this level is suggested by figure 5. And so it goes, on down the line in successively smaller groups, each radiating within its scope.

To man, the mammal, mammals are preëminent subjects of study. Space permits no details here, but it must be added that mammals, too, have diversified enormously and something must be said most briefly as to man's place in this diversity. The extent of mammalian adaptive radiation can be glimpsed by considering kangaroos, moles, bats, monkeys, armadillos, rabbits, mice, whales, cats, elephants, seacows, horses, and giraffes—all mammals along with us. In technical classification the next grade recognized below a class is an order, and conservative students count no fewer than thirty-two orders in the class Mammalia, of which fourteen are extinct and eighteen survive today.

Among these numerous orders is that of the Primates, to which we belong. This order is so primitive in many ways that it is hard to characterize, but even unprogressive members show a tendency toward using the hands to manipulate objects

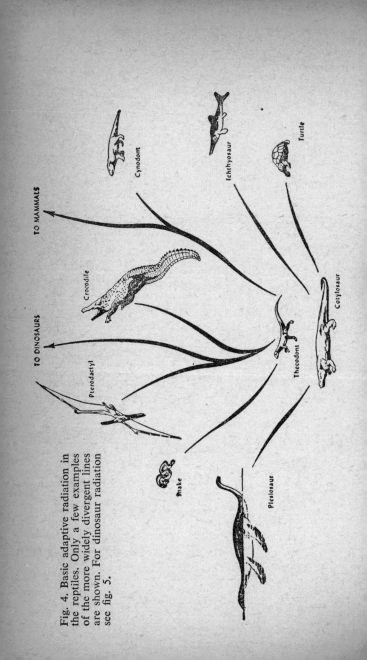

Fig. 4. Basic adaptive radiation in the reptiles. Only a few examples of the more widely divergent lines are shown. For dinosaur radiation see fig. 5.

Fig. 5. Adaptive radiation of the dinosaurs. Only a few of the many divergent lines are shown.

Struthiomimus

Tyrannosaurus

Brontosaurus

Stegosaurus

Ankylosaurus

Corythosaurus

Triceratops

in coördination with the sense of vision, and this is among the basic primate characters. Oddly enough—or, at least, man is likely to think it odd—the early primates and their least modified modern descendants are not particularly intelligent. Yet there is a tendency toward high intelligence in the more progressive lines of primates, and the order does include the highest brain development yet attained by any form of life.

Fig. 6. Representatives of the main groups of primates. The lemur represents the prosimians; the capuchin monkey, the South American monkeys or ceboids; the macaque, the Old World monkeys or cercopithecoids; the chimpanzee, an ape, and the man both represent the broadly manlike or hominoid group. Each group includes a variety of different forms, only one of which is shown as an example.

Broadly speaking, there are four major sorts of primates, exemplified in figure 6. The primates, too, have undergone adaptive radiation, indeed a whole series of radiations. The prosimians, first to arise, radiated early in the Cenozoic, the Age of Mammals. Of these early lines, many became extinct.

A few survived without deep change and represent the prosimian type today. Others progressed in various ways and gave rise to higher forms, monkeys, apes, and men, at different levels of progression and in various geographic regions. The general pattern of this history is suggested by figure 7.

Fig. 7. A representation of primate history and the origin of man as a series of adaptive radiations in space and time.

Looking back over the whole, tremendous panorama of the history of life, now so briefly reviewed from the dim origins down to man, certain broad processes and impressions become evident. There is a trend toward increase and radiation into all possible ways of life, a principle of addition and multiplication. Within the phyla and increasingly within smaller groups there is frequent replacement of older groups by younger, a principle of substitution. There is also extinction; a principle of subtraction, almost universal among detailed types, less frequent for broader grades of organization and practically non-operative at highest levels.

All of these definable processes are evident in the record, and still there is also an impression of a certain disorder or, at least, lack of uniform plan. Addition, multiplication, substitution, and subtraction do not appear constantly or interact to produce clear patterns. There is an odd randomness in the record, a suggestion that it involves a sort of insensate opportunism. There is a lack of fixed plan in detail, but a tendency to spread and fill the earth with life whenever and however this chanced to become possible.

Yet not all is random. We know (or let us grant such knowledge at this point) that change must have direction and cause, and we feel a need to evaluate changes and their causes. From this brief and superficial examination of the record of life let us pass to an attempt to interpret it more profoundly, and first to the question as to what sorts of causes may be operating in the tangled fabric of evolution.

2. The Problem of Problems

WHAT FORCES HAVE BEEN acting throughout the history of life? This is the problem of problems for evolution and for life itself.

Are these the same forces that act throughout the material universe, different in their results only to the extent that the matter on which they are acting is differently organized? Or do they include forces peculiar to and inherent in life, essentially different from the mechanistic forces of cause and effect in the purely material realm? Or, again, do they involve some principle that transcends both matter and life itself, a force that brings about progression toward foreordained goals, and that not only negates but also reverses materialistic cause and effect so that effect precedes cause?

Each of these questions has been answered affirmatively by one or another scientist or philosopher. They embody the three main possibilities in the solution of the problem of problems and each has its ardent supporters. The first solution is that of the materialist, or mechanist, or causalist—the terms are not synonymous but in this connection they designate roughly congruous philosophical points of view. The second solution is that of the vitalist, the student who maintains basic distinction between the principles and forces reflected in vital and those reflected in material phenomena. Adherents of the third solution are almost always also vitalists in this sense (although in fact there is no logical necessity for them to be such), and this solution has commonly been considered no more than another of the innumerable varieties of vitalism. It adds, however, an alternative that differs from vitalism alone as profoundly as vitalism does from materialism. If life, as the vitalists submit, has its own, nonmaterial forces, it does not necessarily follow that these tend toward a final goal or achieve a transcendental purpose. That life, or that the whole cosmos, does have such a finality is the view of the finalist.

There has been a great deal of misunderstanding and name

calling among the materialists, vitalists, and finalists. The vitalists and finalists usually impute to the materialists the views that there is nothing in the universe but pure mechanism and that there is no essential difference between life and nonlife. Some materialists have accepted these imputations and have attempted to defend these propositions. Their purely or merely mechanistic view was more popular a generation or two ago, arising in the first enthusiasm over the great nineteenth-century discoveries in science, than it is today, but it still has able supporters. Others have found this viewpoint indefensible, scientifically or philosophically, and have decided that they were, after all, vitalists rather than materialists, vitalists of some special sort, adherents of "emergent vitalism" or "monistic vitalism."

Now it is merely silly to maintain that there is no essential difference between life and nonlife. The vitalist is naïve indeed who proclaims the discovery of such a difference and concludes that because living organisms operate otherwise than if they were not alive, therefore materialism is wrong and life is a new element or a vital principle or what not. This, the common argument against materialism as it is defined by its opponents, is analogous to claiming that there is a "fire substance" or "fire principle" because fire has properties and phenomena peculiar to it and absent in nonfire. This, indeed, was the theory of our ancestors who gave the name "phlogiston" to the supposed fire element or principle,[1] very much in the same way that some vitalists have given names such as "entelechy" to a hypothetical life element or principle. We know that fire is not such a separate element or principle but that it is a process and organization of matter in which the behavior of matter is different from that in nonfire. Similarly, the materialistic view is not abandoned when life is seen as a process and organization in which the behavior of matter is different from that in its nonliving state.

Granting, as any reasonable person must, that there is an important difference between life and nonlife, you may, if you wish, call the different behavior of matter in life "vitalistic," but this accomplishes nothing and means nothing that was not already obvious. It is an example of the naming fallacy to call this an explanation or a contribution to evolutionary theory. The real issue between materialists and vitalists is not whether life has its own principles and functions, a proposition admitted by most modern materialists and (it seems to

---

[1] This fascinating aberration and the long struggle to correct it are worthy of close study by anyone interested in problems of truth and error. See any good history of science, such as A. Wolf, *A History of Science, Technology, and Philosophy in the Eighteenth Century* (New York, Macmillan, 1939).

me) self-evident. This sort of "emergent" as opposed to "sub-stantive" vitalism[2] is embraced within most of the less crude brands of materialism. A valid issue arises only as regards substantive or dualistic vitalism, the view that there is a life substance or principle which is independent of and in addition to the substances found in inorganic nature and the laws of their behavior. On the other hand, the distinctive claim of materialism is not stupid denial of special attributes to life, but the view that the substances and the principles involved in organic evolution are those universal in the material world and that the distinctive attributes and activities of life are inherent in its organization only.

This clarification is essential in the marshaling of evidence that may bear, one way or another, on choice between materialistic and vitalistic interpretation of the history of life. Beyond this are further, more philosophical implications, to be discussed more fully in the last four chapters of this book but to be mentioned here in passing to forestall possible mis-apprehension. The view of life as mere mechanism or autom-atism represents one extreme of the general field of ma-terialism, an extreme now rather widely abandoned by materialists. It is compatible with materialism to hold that life and the universe involve more than objective material and mechanism. At one end of the enquiry the origin and nature of the existing materials and mechanisms have no evident materialistic explanation even though, given these as existing, their operation may be purely materialistic. At the other end the possibility is not excluded that, within the unique organ-ization of matter that is life, these operations may develop choice, values, and moral judgment. The existence of these qualities is also a basic tenet of most vitalist theories, which tend, however, to maintain that they are inherent in, rather than developed by, life.

The distinctive finalist belief is that of progression toward a goal or end. The end is not reached, the finalist believes, because of what goes before, but what goes before is but a means for reaching the end. The end, although later in time, is, then, the cause and the preceding course of history is the effect. The history of life is thus to be viewed as purposeful, and (it almost goes without saying) finalists usually consider man as the essential feature of that purpose. Such a view is not necessarily inconsistent with materialism: the forces of history could be materialistic and yet have been instituted as a means for reaching an end. Finalists more commonly, how-ever, hold subsidiary opinions that are vitalistic rather than

[2] See for example, C. D. Broad, *The Mind and Its Place in Nature* (New York, Harcourt, Brace, 1925).

materialistic. The purposefulness of evolution is considered inherent in, or special to, life, or an essential vital essence is seen as a means of reaching the goal.

Scientists and particularly the professional students of evolution are often accused of a bias toward mechanism or materialism,[3] even though believers in vitalism and in finalism are not lacking among them. Such bias as may exist is inherent in the method of science. The most successful scientific investigation has generally involved treating phenomena *as if* they were purely materialistic, rejecting any metaphysical hypothesis as long as a physical hypothesis seems possible. The method works. The restriction is necessary because science is confined to physical means of investigation and so it would stultify its own efforts to postulate that its subject is not physical and so not susceptible to its methods. Yet few scientists would maintain that the required restrictions of their methods necessarily delimit all truth or that the materialistic nature of their hypotheses imposes materialism on the universe.

Although the metaphysical cannot be directly investigated by the methods of science, its results may be. It is, indeed, one of the greatest values of our present subject that it can serve as a means of testing the fundamental philosophies of materialism, vitalism, and finalism. Vitalism and finalism involve elements postulated as beyond the reach of purely material scientific investigation. Yet the truth of these philosophies would involve material consequences in the history of life. The investigation of these possible consequences is within the scope of scientific method, which therefore can provide evidence on which to base a choice among materialism, vitalism, and finalism, as well as among the variety of particular theories that have been elaborated within the framework of each of these philosophies. Conviction as to the essential truth of materialism need not, then, be the result of bias or of the limitations of the scientific method, but may be the result of careful evaluation of evidence. A scientific bias cheerfully confessed is the belief that the results of such evaluation are likely to be nearer the truth than are the inclinations of personal preference or the traditions of a less knowledgeable and less critical past.

Such phenomena of evolution as should provide particular

[3] See for instance E. S. Russell's witty and persuasive but oddly inconclusive book, *The Directiveness of Organic Activities* (Cambridge, England, University Press, 1945). Russell ridicules the mechanistic bias of scientists and proclaims that the causal-analytical method is quite inadequate for the study of the activity of life. He develops a finalist thesis on the basis of the directiveness or purposiveness of life activities which are said not to be reducible to "activities of a lower order," i.e., nonvital. He energetically maintains that such a view is neither materialistic nor vitalistic. Yet by any definition known to me his finalism is vitalistic. Denial of this produces no alternative to it.

crucial evidence of this sort are now to be especially considered. The field of evolution in all its various phenomena and
processes is so vast that selection must be exercised. An
acceptable general theory of evolution must be prepared to
explain all these phenomena, or at least to demonstrate that
such explanation is a reasonable probability within its framework. All, however, are not equally crucial for the evaluation
of the proposed theories. Certain aspects of evolution are
evidently particularly likely to reveal possible underlying general causes and to help to discriminate between these as to
their reality or probability. In the long quarrel between materialists and vitalists it has, for instance, been recognized on
both sides that the phenomenon of orientation in evolution—
of the real or apparent tendency for evolution to proceed
along limited, directional paths—is crucial for any eventual
decision between the schools. It is such lines of evidence as
this that require particularly critical discussion now.

It will hardly be supposed that all materialists, all vitalists,
or all finalists have been in agreement among themselves. On
the contrary, within each broad school of thought the most
diverse shades of opinion have existed, and two general
theories as to the causes of evolution may both be, for instance, thoroughly materialistic and yet stand in strong contradiction to each other. Only less important than choice
among the broader philosophies is critical evaluation of these
many theories. Evidence for such evaluation will also be
sought in dealing with processes of evolution in the following
pages, and an historical summary and attempted judgment of
the more important of these theories will follow.

3. Oriented Evolution

A WIDELY held opinion regarding the course of evolution has
been that it tends to occur in straight lines, that once a certain
sort of structural change has started in a given group this
tends to continue without deviation indefinitely or to the
extinction of that group. The example most often given is
that of the change from eohippus to the modern horse, *Equus,*
represented as involving a gradual increase in size, reduction
in number of toes, increase in height and complication of
teeth, and generally a transformation of all characters of
eohippus to those of *Equus* in a steady, undeviating way. It
happens that this usual example has been badly misrepre-

sented. Things did not, as a matter of observable fact, occur in just that way in the history of the horse. Yet the fact remains that the sequence cannot be considered random. The changes involved do have direction and orientation, even though these were not as regular as they have usually been represented. And so, in hundreds or thousands of other cases, it seems clear that there is an orientation of some sort.

The record as a whole gave an effect of opportunism, of divergence into nearly all available ways of life, yet this in itself is an oriented rather than a random process. Examined in greater detail, the record seems still less to be purely random, and descent within any one line usually gives the impression of being rather stringently oriented in many, although commonly not in all, of its features. There are, also, sorts of structural changes so widespread in different lines that they seem to represent general tendencies, a common orientation, or so-called "laws" of evolution. (Like human laws, the "laws" of evolution are often broken and, indeed, they are human constructions which we impose on the complex phenomena of nature and which nature is under no obligation to follow.) Among these, one of the best substantiated is a tendency for increase in size. Little eohippus and big *Equus* provide, again, a familiar example. Others may be found in almost any group of animals: medium-sized Eocene and Oligocene proboscideans and their enormous Pleistocene and Recent successors among mastodons, mammoths, and elephants; relatively little Triassic dinosaurs and the gargantuan Jurassic and Cretaceous forms; small Cambrian sea snails working up to forms six inches or more in height in the Mississippian and to truly enormous sizes in later and Recent times—in familiar example, the conchs so abundant off the Florida keys.

The widespread occurrence of oriented evolution being established, questions arise as to just how characteristic it is, whether universal, usual, or only occasional, the existence and nature of exceptions, the relationship of oriented evolution to environmental factors, and other enquiries leading up to the question as to what orienting force or forces are involved. On this last point the main alternatives are whether orientation, or change in a straight line, is something inherent in life and its evolution, a hypothesis held in common by most vitalists and finalists; or whether it is dependent only on the physical possibilities of the situation and on the interplay of organism and environment, the usual materialist hypothesis. In the first case, orientation should be universal or nearly so except, perhaps, when gross environmental fluctuations make it quite impossible. It should normally be not merely direc-

tional but unidirectional, that is, not merely tending in some
direction but long maintaining a single direction. Above all,
it should not fluctuate in a constant or regular way according
to the adaptive advantage to the animals concerned and there
should be instances when the long trend in one direction is
inadaptive finally or throughout, that is, harmful rather than
useful to the harmonious functioning of the animals in their
environments. On the other hand, under the various materialistic hypotheses, orientation may be expected to be less rigid,
to have many exceptions, to allow numerous changes and
even occasional reversals in direction of evolution, and to be
related, on the whole, to adaptive advantage for the animals
concerned.

It is easy enough, in the first place, to observe that evolution along straight lines, or even the rigid orientation of evolution in a less simple way, is far from universal. It is only a
tendency with so many exceptions as hardly to constitute a
rule.

Differences in rate, kind, and direction of evolutionary
changes are strikingly characteristic of the true facts in the
prime example constantly cited as supposed proof that evolution occurs without such differences, in an orthogenetic[1] way:
the horse family. Consider the main trends in evolution of
horse teeth, for instance. One type of change in them was a
tendency for premolars and molars to become more alike—
all but the first premolar—with the result that six cheek teeth,
three premolars and three molars, have come to have almost
the same pattern. This went on rather steadily during the
Eocene, reached essential completion at the end of that epoch,
and then stopped. Another change was complication and, in
other ways, alteration in the pattern of the molars (and of
the premolars, as they became more like molars). This went
on in a fluctuating way but in a single line from eohippus
through the Eocene and Oligocene—in a single line only to
the extent that the evolving group in America, which eventually gave rise to *Equus,* was then a single line of major populations. Other lines from eohippus occurred in Europe, and
even in the Eocene these gave rise to diverse lines with quite
different tooth patterns. Then in the Miocene the hitherto
unified American line of the horse family split into five (or,
according to some students even more) major branches, con-

[1] Evolution in a straight line is commonly called "orthogenesis" and will be
found discussed under that title in most books on evolution. The term has, however,
been kicked around so much that hardly any two students mean exactly the same
thing when they use it. To some it means little more than that evolution is not
completely random. To others, use of the term implies granting the whole finalist
thesis of undeviating progress toward a goal. Arguments over orthogenesis are unduly
obscured and complicated by entirely unimportant semantic difficulties. It usually is
understood, however, to mean a postulated inner urge or inherent tendency for
evolution to continue in a given direction.

temporaneous genera, *each* of which had a distinct and characteristic molar pattern. Some of these tended to have simpler patterns than their ancestry, and some more complicated. Another split into at least five distinct lineages and again each developed a different sort of pattern, varying but now all more or less comparable in degree of complication. In height of teeth, too, the various lines in the Miocene and Pliocene differed radically. In some the teeth remained low, increasing, if at all, only in correlation with the sizes of the animals. One

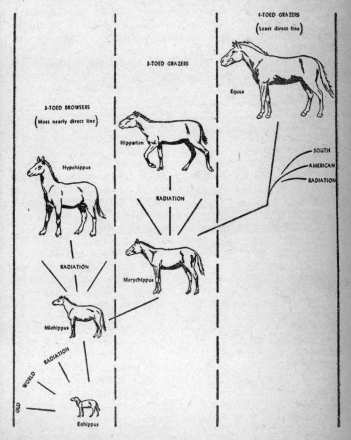

Fig. 8. The evolution of the horse family. The animals shown are only a few of many in the family, and lines of evolution were more numerous and complex than here indicated in detail. The various forms are drawn to the same scale.

Miocene line rapidly developed exceptionally high teeth. This was not a continuation of the "orthogenetic" trend of the Eocene and Oligocene horses but a new direction of evolution. Although there is, in fact, no strictly straight line of horse evolution, the nearest thing to one leads not from eohippus to *Equus* but from eohippus to an extinct group, decidedly different from the living horses, called *Hypohippus*. (See fig. 8.)

Every feature of horse evolution tells a comparably complex story if this is examined in detail and in all the divergent lines of the horse family. The feet, to supplement the example here, hardly evolved at all in the Eocene, then evolved rapidly to a basic three-toed Oligocene type which remained nearly static in some later lines, in others evolved gradually to different three-toed types mechanically sounder for larger animals, and in one line only finally evolved rapidly in one phase to a one-toed type. This, again, did not really continue the usual trend among the three-toed types but was a new evolutionary direction for them. In the particular lineage from eohippus to *Equus,* general foot mechanics became first more complex, then simpler. The number of toes did not change at even pace from four (in the forefoot) to one, but changed in two spurts, first from four to three, then much later from three to one, each rapid transition followed by slower mechanical adjustment to the new sort of foot and to changes in the weights of the animals.[2]

The horses even provide us with exceptions to the rule that animals tend to increase in size in their evolution. During the Eocene the record, contrary to a rather general impression, does not show any net or average increase in size. In fact the known late Eocene horses average rather smaller than eohippus in the early Eocene. Then still later, in the Miocene and Pliocene, there were at least three different branches of the horse family characterized by decrease in size (*Archaeohippus, Nannippus, Calippus*), while at the same time other lines were, according to "rule," increasing in size. At that time, too, others were fluctuating around a mean size without notable change and still others developed different species of decidedly different sizes—as, indeed, is the case in *Equus* today.

There is increasing evidence that mammals in general, es-

[2] Details of these and other changes in horse evolution as it really occurred are rather fully set forth in the technical literature. Unfortunately, however, more general and popularized accounts have usually tried to simplify the story by omitting the real diversity of horse evolution and discussing it *as if* it were a case of orthogenesis. Even paleontologists who have not handled the actual specimens or digested the great volume of very technical publications have been usually seriously misled by this spurious simplification. I have elsewhere tried to give a more up-to-date and less misleading nontechnical account of this crucial example of evolution in action in *Horses* (New York, Oxford University Press, 1951).

pecially some of the relatively large forms, have tended to decrease in average size since the Pleistocene ice age.[3] In itself this negates any invariability in the rule of increase of size, and it certainly strongly suggests adaptive response to climatic conditions as opposed to size control by some inner tendency or life urge within the organisms alone. We know that climates have tended to become warmer since the Pleistocene. We also know that closely related living mammals show the adaptive phenomenon of being, on an average, relatively smaller in warmer climates. It is certainly reasonable to suppose that this is the same sort of phenomenon involved in size decrease from Pleistocene to Recent.

In this connection, it is known that many large animals of the past became extinct and are not the ancestors of their smaller living relatives. Mammoths were not ancestral to smaller elephants. (As a matter of fact, most mammoths were no larger than some living elephants, but a few were.) The elephantine ground sloths were not ancestral to the little living tree sloths. The dinosaurs were not the ancestors of the small lizards of later times. But this does not mean that forms that *were* the ancestors of living animals were not also somewhat larger than the latter at one time or another, and such does appear to be the case for some of them.

Some paleontologists have been so impressed by the frequent trend for animals to become larger as times goes on that they have tried to work it the other way around. If they find, say, a Pleistocene bison that is somewhat larger than a Recent bison (so-called *Bison taylori,* associate and prey of early man in America, is a good example), then they conclude that it is not ancestral to later bison *because* it is larger. You can establish any "rule" you like if you start with the rule and then interpret the evidence accordingly.

This suggests some brief digressive but pertinent remarks on certain psychological factors in the interpretation of the necessarily imperfect evolutionary record. A really complete evolutionary lineage is never preserved; this would mean fossilization and recovery of all the animals that ever lived as parts of that lineage, an absurdly impossible chance. Museum curators know that even if the miracle of fossilization occurred, recovery and study would be impossible if only on grounds of expense. The actual data, then, normally consist of relatively small samples of the lineage, scattered more or less at random in space and time. The process of interpretation consists of connecting these samples in a way necessarily

---

[3] The evidence has not all been compiled in one place, as yet, but it already is practically conclusive for some groups and strongly suggestive of a general trend. See, for instance, D. A. Hooijer, "Mammalian Evolution in the Quaternary of Southern and Eastern Asia" (*Evolution, 3* [1949], 125-128).

more or less subjective, and students may use the same data
to "prove" diametrically opposed theories. Thus with data like
those schematically shown in figure 9A, one student may believe that evolution is always or basically orthogenetic. He will
then conclude that the samples represent variations around a
series of different straight lines of evolution, perhaps from
four different lineages, with the earlier parts unknown for the
later lines (figure 9B). Having composed this figure, he will
adduce it as evidence that evolution is orthogenetic.[4]

Another student may hold the opinion that evolution is a
discontinuous process, consisting of leaps from one level

Fig. 9. A hypothetical example of known facts of animal history
and various ways of interpreting them. A (upper left), observed
facts. B (upper right), interpretation as a series of separate orthogenetic lines. C (lower left), interpretation as a sequence of
stages with each arising by one leap, without transition. D (lower right), interpretation as a single line of evolution, changing
in direction.

or group to another, without intermediate forms. He will
then interpret these samples more or less as shown in figure
9C, and in turn will claim that this record is evidence for
his theory.[5]

[4] The example is diagrammatic but not imaginary. See, for instance the inter-
pretations of lineages of mastodons and elephants in H. F. Osborn's *Proboscidea*
(New York, American Museum of Natural History, 2 vols.: 1936, 1942).

[5] Closely analogous examples of subjective arrangement of evidence to favor this
type of theory may be found, for instance, in O. H. Schindewolf, *Grundfragen der
Paläontologie* (Stuttgart, Schweizerbart [Nägele], 1950).

Still another student will notice that the over-all pattern of these samples is, in fact, oriented or correlated in time and in structure, although not in a straight line. Interpreting the line of descent as in figure 9D, he will consider this evidence for the theory that evolution is a continuous, oriented, but not inherently orthogenetic process.

Each student thus actually puts his particular theory into the data, and it is not surprising that each then gets his own theory out of these data when he is through. This does not, however, mean that such evidence is valueless, or that one theory is as good, as probable, as another. It explains diversity of opinion among competent students and shows how all can cite evidence for their conflicting theories. The evidence for his views may be persuasive as adduced by any one student, and yet when all theories are considered together the evidence may quite clearly favor one theory over another. In the hypothetical example of figure 9, which I believe is a fair representation of the general character of a great number of real examples, it seems evident that the interpretive pattern shown in D is more probable, on the face of the data, than B and C. D is less subjective: the trend it shows is objectively present even if B or C should also prove to be present. It is the most probable inference on sound statistical principles. It, alone of the three, follows the famous maxim of William of Occam, fundamental in logic and in scientific investigation, that entities (in theories or hypotheses) are not to be multiplied unnecessarily.

Although in cases like this example any of the conflicting theories *may* be true, there are other cases in which one of them *must,* within reason, be true. It does not wholly follow that the same theory *must* also be true in all cases where others *may* be, but a strong probability is certainly established. Such decisive examples do exist for our present subject. The horse family is one. Incomplete as they are, the data are so abundant and, aside from one or two minor points, so completely continuous that it is fair to say that they *cannot* be fitted to an interpretation of type B or C in figure 9. They certainly represent a sequence like D of that figure, complicated only by the presence of repeated branching which is fully consistent with the theory symbolized by D and largely inconsistent with those of B or C.

It is easy enough to see that, in evolution as a whole, departure from a straight-line pattern must have been exceedingly frequent. Every rise of a distinctively new adaptive type among organisms *necessarily* represents a change in direction of evolution. A fish evolving in a constant direction remains a fish and does not become an amphibian. Whales, which certainly arose from quadrupedal land mammals, cannot by any juggling of the data be represented as arising by continuation of the trend that gave rise to quadrupedal mammals. Bipedal man must equally represent a new trend, a decided change in evolutionary direction from that giving rise to his quadrupedal ancestors.

Similarly each of the many thousands of major and minor adaptive types arising in the evolution of life represents a change, large or small, in the direction of evolution. Strictly straight-line evolution is confined to relatively minor progressions within established types. Even here this phenomenon seems less common than claimed by those who impose an orthogenetic pattern on any sequence too imperfect to exclude this possibility. Adequately known sequences rarely show this sort of purposeful-looking progression straight toward an end which might be a goal. The most nearly direct evolutionary lines seem almost always to be short, geologically speaking. And any curve seems nearly straight if only a short segment of it is seen.

The extreme view that evolution is basically or over all an orthogenetic process is evidence that some scientists' minds tend to move in straight lines,[6] not that evolution does. The grand fact is that rigid orientation of evolutionary change in a single direction is not inherent in the evolutionary process or even particularly characteristic of it, and yet that the process is not fully random. Orientation is usual, but the directions diverge for different groups, and for single lineages the direction may, so to speak, twist and turn in a remarkable way. *Something* operates in evolution to keep changes, for greater or less periods, progressive within delimited paths, but these paths may not be straight and may have unexpected ends.

There are, of course, certain limitations always present in any existing situation. Evolution fully at random in an unlimited, or even in a very large, number of directions is never possible to a group of organisms. Changes in size of whole organisms or of various of their parts are probably the commonest sort of evolutionary change, and such evolution can be in only one of two directions: toward larger or smaller. There is no conceivable alternative. More subtly, given a metabolic system that requires intake of oxygen, the evolution of a group of animals is limited to environments where oxygen is present and to such structural changes as

[6] In a session on orthogenesis at a recent international conference on evolutionary problems held in Paris, an eminent student startled his colleagues by proclaiming that evolution consists of nothing but millions of orthogenetic lines. This is the most extreme case of orthomania, or straight lines before the eyes, known to me, but milder cases of this affliction are fairly common.

retain or provide apparatus for extracting oxygen in that environment. Without change of environment, a deep sea fish cannot evolve lungs nor an eagle gills. Profound limitations on possible directions of evolution for any group of organisms are imposed by two indisputable factors universally present: surviving organisms must meet the minimum requirements of life in an available environment, and changes can only occur on the basis of what already exists. The environments available are not limitless, and each permits survival on its own terms only. At any time the possibilities for future change within a given group are also always limited by what the organisms have already become; their past is one of the determinants of their future. Evolution is amazingly versatile in adapting the materials at hand to other uses, as will be seen later on, but its possibilities are always limited by the nature of those materials and by the external requirements for survival.

Even these broad, rather obvious limitations suggest strongly that orientation in evolution is not determined solely by some characteristic within the evolving organisms or solely by external factors in their environment, but by both and by interplay between the two.

It is an old theory, probably the first really scientific theory of evolution to be proposed, that changes in groups of organisms are not merely limited but also directly induced by changes in the environment. If this were true, then the environment alone would be the orienting factor in evolution, the nonrandom or antichance factor that clearly does exist somewhere in the process. The theory finds support in the universal integration of organisms into their environments, the evident close correspondence between most of their structures and activities and the needs imposed by their places in nature. It is clear enough that environment must have something to do with the orientation of evolution, but the idea that it is the direct or sole *cause* of oriented change has broken down and has had to be abandoned by almost all free students of evolution.[7] In the wide picture of life on the earth the evidence is all against any general and continuous change of environment alone that could account for the sort of change in life that has occurred. In particular instances of environmental change, evolving organisms do not

---

[7] "*Almost* all" does not really mean that the theory needs still to be very seriously considered. So diverse and erratic are the operations of the human mind that no theory is likely completely to lack supporters. After all, there are still people who believe that the sun goes around the earth and who have strong arguments for this view.

"Free students" included eminent Soviet scientists prior to the 1948 intellectual purge. The reactionism of Lysenko has returned to the disproven environmental theory on political, not scientific, grounds.

respond in a uniform way, as if the environment were causing changes in structure. Moreover we now have a great deal
of experience as to how heritable changes in organisms actually do appear, and there is the strongest sort of evidence
that they do not appear as direct responses in kind to environmental influences.

On the other hand, it has already been shown that inherent
tendencies for organisms to evolve in fixed directions regardless of the environment cannot be the whole story either, and
more evidence against this view will appear as the enquiry
continues. The most promising clue seems to lie in the inter-
relationship between organism and environment, and not in
one or the other of these alone. This functional interrelation-
ship is adaptation, one of the major features of evolution
and of life. The environmental presence of dissolved oxygen
in water and the internal physiological system of fishes based
on intake of oxygen are interrelated by the adaptation of
gills (and a whole complex of associated structures), which
remove oxygen from the water and supply it to the internal
system of the fish. The marvelous mechanism of the human
hand is an adaptation to perform functions eminently useful
in the human environment. The fangs of a wolf are an adaptation to environmental requirements for defense and offense.
Examples of such relationships are so extremely widespread
and so well known to everyone that it is needless to multiply
them here.

The key to the adaptive nature of any characteristic of
an organism is its usefulness under the conditions in which
the organism lives. Just here it does not particularly matter
how this relationship arises, although of course that is one
of the main objects of our enquiry. Whatever we may later
decide to be its cause, the fact is that adaptation, by the criterion of usefulness, certainly does occur. Every organism
has innumerable adaptive characteristics. This is one of the
most universal features of living things. The present point
is to decide whether adaptation is the orienting factor in
evolution. If so, continuing trends in evolution should be
adaptive in character. The changes involved should be useful to the organisms. This usefulness may be in better fitness
for the way of life already followed by the organisms, or
may enable them to cope with imposed changes in that way
of life, or may permit (or accompany) shift to some other
way of life.

Examples make these possibilities more concrete. Ability
to run faster, a trend in herbivore evolution—although, as
usual, not universal or constant—is evidently useful, that is,
adaptive, in the way of life of animals dependent mainly on

speed for safety. As their prey thus becomes swifter, a change in the way of life of carnivores is imposed on them: it becomes advantageous, adaptive, for them also to run faster or to develop methods of attack from ambush or other ways of coping with the increased speed of the herbivores. There are trends observable in the orientation of carnivore evolution, in various lines. Among herbivores, again, as competition for food becomes severe among the browsers, living on succulent or leafy herbage, it becomes advantageous for some of them to shift to a different way of life, eating some other sort of food such as grass. This adaptive trend to a new sort of adaptation is prominent in one phase of horse evolution, when high-crowned grazing teeth arose. (It is typical of such shifts in adaptive type that the phase was short, the shift relatively rapid.) Some carnivores showed analogous shifts, with adaptive trends toward new ways of life as regards food habits; an extreme example is the rise of a strictly vegetarian "carnivore," the panda.

If, on the other hand, adaptation is not the only or at least the dominant orienting factor in evolution, then there should be recorded clear-cut and probably numerous examples of trends that are not adaptive in nature. We should expect to find long-continued changes of no apparent use to the organisms. The qualification "long-continued" is necessary here because there certainly are shorter, random, non-oriented phases in evolution, which constitute a distinct problem for later discussion. We should expect, especially if we happen to be finalists, that eventually useful characteristics may appear and become trends before they are useful. We should also expect some trends to persist without reference to changes in habits of the animals exhibiting them. And perhaps most crucial of all, there should be trends, possibly useful in earlier stages, which persist until they are of no further use or become finally downright harmful. These may even be expected to cause extinction in many cases.

No one doubts that there are adaptive trends. These surely exist and are numerous. The question is as to the existence or prevalence of nonadaptive trends. Every type of nonadaptive trend mentioned above has been claimed as existent by students who do not think that evolution is oriented by adaptation, and supposed examples of each have been given by them. It is notoriously impossible to prove that a rule has *no* exceptions, that for instance a nonadaptive trend *never* occurred, for we do not know and no one man could examine the intricacies of all evolutionary trends whatsoever. It is also impossible in reasonable compass to examine each one of the many supposed examples of nonadaptive trends. It is, how-

ever, possible to study outstanding and crucial examples of
the claimed sorts of nonadaptive trends and to base on these
results a reasonable judgment as to the probability of nonadaptive orientation in evolution.[8]

Among supposed examples of nonadaptive trends, the
sabertooths (or saber-toothed "tigers," but they were no more
tigers than they were lions, lynxes, or tabbies), the Irish elk,
the coiled oysters or gryphaeas, the titanotheres, and the
horses are typical, perhaps most often cited, and well cover
the variety of such supposed phenomena. Even these must
be treated briefly here, as each case is so complex as to
merit book-length discussion.

The sabertooth is one of the most famous of animals just
because it is often innocently supposed to be an indisputable
example of an inadaptive trend. In fields far remote from
paleontology the poor sabertooth has come to figure as a
horrible example, a pathetic case history of evolution gone
wrong.[9] Its supposed evidence is thus characteristically summarized in a book on (human) personality: "The long canine
tooth of the saber-toothed tiger grew more and more into
an impossible occlusion. Finally, it was so long that the tiger
could not bite effectively, and the animal became extinct."[10]
Now, like so many things that everyone seems to know, this
is not true. Sabertooths appear in the record in the early
Oligocene, more or less 40,000,000 years ago, and they became extinct only yesterday, around the end of the Pleistocene, 20,000 or 30,000 years ago. The fact is that during
this long span the sabertooths did not show a trend toward
increase in relative size of the canine tooth. It happens that
the earliest sabertooth known (*Eusmilus*) had relatively one
of the largest canines known in the group. (See fig. 10.)
Throughout their history the size of sabertooth canines varied considerably from one group to another but varied about a fairly constant average size, which is exactly
what would be expected if the size were *adaptive* at all times

---

[8] These and other supposed examples may be found in abundance in the writings
of vitalist evolutionists and philosophers, in the attacks on Darwinism and neo-
Darwinism common a generation ago and still continuing in some circles although
largely abated, and in general in espousals of "autogenetic" theories of evolution,
which hold that organisms are self- or auto-evolving and that the orienting factors
are inherent in the organism in some unexplained way. An outstanding and able
example of this school is L. S. Berg's, *Nomogenesis; or Evolution Determined by
Law* (trans. from the Russian by J. N. Rostovstow [London, Constable, 1926]).

[9] For example, S. Brody's interesting and otherwise excellent paper, "Science and
Social Wisdom" (*Sci. Monthly, 59* [1944], 203-214), includes almost total miscom-
prehension of what is really known of sabertooth history.

[10] G. Murphy, *Personality. A Biosocial Approach to Origins and Structure* (New
York and London, Harper, 1947). Dr. Murphy is hardly to be blamed for accepting
what was long a cliché among the less critical of paleontologists. As far as a
nonpsychologist can judge, his book seems one of the most profound and able in
its field, and repetition of such views is not characteristic of it.

Fig. 10. Skulls of saber-toothed "tigers." *Eusmilus*, early Oligocene, is one of the earliest known forms and *Smilodon*, Pleistocene, one of the last. *Eusmilus* is smaller, but the two skulls have
been drawn the same size to permit easier comparison.

and there were no secular trend in adaptive advantage but only local and temporary differences in its details. The biting mechanism in the last sabertooths was still perfectly effective, no less and probably no more so than in the Oligocene.[11] To characterize as finally ineffective a mechanism that persisted without essential change in a group abundant and obviously highly successful for some 40,000,000 years seems quaintly illogical! In short, the "inadaptive trend" of the sabertooth is a mere fairy tale, or more fairly, it was an error based on too facile conclusion from imperfect information and it has since been perpetuated as a scientific legend.

The case of the Irish elk (*Megaloceros*) is more seriously deserving of attention in this connection. This animal represented the extreme development of a group, offshoot of the common European stags (not really elks), in which the size and complexity of the antlers increased until finally they were fantastic. It seems that yearly replacement of these masses of bone must have been a severe physiological burden and that the strain of carrying such a weight on the head must also have been severe. Although there is a total lack of decisive evidence that this development did, in fact, cause extinction of the group, it does seem likely that it was a factor in that extinction. There is nevertheless no real reason at all to think that they were inadaptive *when they arose;* it is conclusively evident that the big sabertooth canines were not inadaptive when they arose. The biggest antlered stags did not flourish as long as the sabertooths, only for a few thousand years, but they did flourish for a while. If the antlers were a factor in extinction, this was very likely because—as eventually, at long last, with the sabertooth canines—changing conditions made them inadaptive after they reached maximum size. In that case the trend up to that size was not inadaptive.

There is, however, an additional or alternative factor in the antler development of this group, that of relative growth. All animals have distinctive growth patterns determined in the main by heredity. In fact, what animals, and plants, too, inherit from their parents are not developed characteristics, such as long noses, blue eyes, or pink flowers, but determiners of a developmental process in the course of which such characteristics eventuate, more or less modified by the conditions under which development occurs. As growth goes on, all parts of the organism do not increase proportionately. Everyone has noticed that human babies have relatively shorter legs but bigger heads than adults. Some parts grow

[11] On this and the basic features of cat evolution in general, see W. D. Matthew's classic paper, "The Phylogeny of the Felidae" (*Bull. Amer. Mus. Nat. Hist., 28* [1910], 289-316).

faster than the body as a whole, some parts at about the same rate and some more slowly. Some may even decrease in absolute size as the body grows: in later stages of human growth the thymus gland normally does this. Stags have a growth pattern in which as the body becomes bigger the antlers become even bigger; they increase not only in absolute size but also in size relative to the body of the animal. In such a group, if there were an evolutionary trend toward larger adult body size, there would also, automatically, be a trend toward relatively larger antlers. The Irish elk had the largest body of any of the deer in this group, and its antlers are just the size to be expected if the inherited relative growth pattern remained the same.[12] The real trend, then, was for increase in total or body size. Antler size just tagged along, or raced ahead, in accordance with a growth pattern evidently adaptive in origin and adaptive in living stags. The body size increase in these great extinct stags was probably adaptive throughout, whether or not it carried antler size to an inadaptive degree, which remains a moot point.

It is the most reasonable view, at least, that increase in gross size, which is among the most widespread of trends in animal evolution, is oriented by adaptation. It is commonly advantageous for an animal to be slightly larger than others of its kind: the larger animal will be a little faster, a little stronger; in accordance with relative growth, it may have and be able to handle more effective weapons for offense or defense; it will, on an average, have more cells in the body, with increased opportunity for complication or differentiation of tissues and organs; under some conditions, such as cold climate for warm-blooded animals, it will have improved thermal efficiency. The advantage will not be very great, and any considerable difference in size may be disadvantageous because, for instance, of disharmony in development, undue food needs, and disparity with other members of the species. We find, in fact, that the trend is usually slow and gradual, not in sudden steps. It also occurs in just those situations where we would expect it to be advantageous. On the other hand, there are conditions in which increase in size is disadvantageous; in most burrowing animals or those depending for safety on obscurity and hiding in small places; in one-celled animals, above certain low limits, because there is no special means of circulation of metabolic supplies and products; in other animals for which (as there is finally for every animal) there is a limit of size beyond which mechanics

---

[12] Although the subject has been greatly elaborated and many more of its implications explored in later work, the best general treatment of relative growth, including that of antlers, continues to be J. S. Huxley's *Problems of Relative Growth* (London, Methuen, 1932).

and physiology cease to be efficient; in many types of flying animals (notably among insects) where the difficulty of supporting weight soon overbalances any advantage of greater size; in animals on islands or elsewhere where food supply is rigidly limited and greater use by each individual would reduce the size of the breeding population unduly. It is in just such groups that the "law" of size increase is suspended or repealed and that we find persistently small organisms, or reversal of trend from larger to smaller—as when elephants become stranded on islands. The rule of size increase in evolution operates in general as if it were thoroughly adaptive. If in special cases we cannot know for certain whether it is adaptive or not, we may properly assume that it is, unless clear evidence to the contrary exists. No such contrary evidence does exist in the case of the Irish stag or any other animal known to me. Throughout the world of life the adjustment of size to the effective following of a way of life is remarkably precise.[13]

The combination of adaptive size trends with relative growth produces simultaneous trends which may also be adaptive, or may be nonadaptive (of no particular advantage or disadvantage), or inadaptive (disadvantageous), as long as the disadvantage does not overbalance the advantage of being of the best gross size. This apparently accounts for most of the cases of apparently meaningless or disadvantageous features in oriented evolution. There are other ways, too, in which inadaptive change of a particular character may be merely a secondary result of a trend that is really adaptive.[14]

The example of the evolution of the coiled oysters has analogies with that of the sabertooths and of the Irish elk and need not now detain us long. At various times during the Mesozoic several different lineages of oysters recurrently developed a trend toward curling of one of the two shells into a plane spiral. (See fig. 11.) The highly coiled types are collectively called *Gryphaea*. In each case the trend is short in geological time. It went on rapidly until the shells had one-and-a-half turns, more or less, in the oldest shells, and then

[13] The argument, to this point, does not depend on whether the organisms have their way of life because they are the right size or are the right size because they have this way of life. I think neither statement is quite correct, but in any case the result is size adaptation.

[14] For discussion of some of these other rather more abstruse processes see, for instance, my *Tempo and Mode in Evolution* (New York, Columbia University Press, 1944) or B. Rensch's *Neuere Probleme der Abstammungslehre* (Stuttgart, F. Enke, 1947). There is also some discussion of this aspect of trends in Huxley's important work on *Evolution. The Modern Synthesis* (New York and London, Harper, 1942), which in every chapter has much that is pertinent to our present enquiry.

each line became extinct. In extreme cases the coiled shell grew around until it pressed on the other shell and they could not be separated. When this happened the animal inside must have died, because it needs to separate the shells slightly in order to take in food and water and to expel waste products. According to one opinion, this trend was not adaptive or, if adaptive in early stages, was carried so far as to cause extinction because all the animals sealed themselves up in their shells and so died.

The trend probably was adaptive. A coiled shell is advantageous for an oyster in soft mud, and that seems to be the environment in which the gryphaeoid trends primarily occurred. There is really no good reason to believe that the change was carried to an inadaptive degree by the trend.

Fig. 11. Evolution of a coiled oyster, *Gryphaea*, right, from an oyster of more usual type, left. (Redrawn with some modification after Trueman.)

Death by self-immurement came only to extreme variant individuals in their old age. As far as evolution is concerned, among nonsocial animals what happens to nonbreeders or to old animals that have finished their share of breeding makes no difference at all. (It is one of the radical differences in evolutionary processes caused by the development of social structures that in these the nonbreeders and those past breeding age may have a decided influence on evolution of the group.) It is also probable that a relative growth factor is involved and that coiling became stronger and had an earlier onset as the final size of the animals increased. In that case the last evolutionary stage represented a compromise between the best size, perhaps not yet reached, and the best degree of coiling, perhaps already somewhat exceeded. In any case, commitment to so special a type of structure or compromise between two concurrent trends may well have caused extinction as conditions changed and competitors developed; but this does not warrant the conclusion that the trends, while they continued, were anything but strictly adaptive.[15]

Supposed instances of nonadaptive trends in evolution may also concern the beginning rather than the end of such trends as in the preceding examples. The suggestion that characteristics later of great usefulness to their possessors may arise without any adaptive value and increase in a trend

Fig. 12. Evolution of titanothere horns. Only a few of many different lines are shown. (Data from Osborn.)

before this value develops is particularly related to the finalist thesis. The titanotheres provide a typical and often-cited example of this supposed phenomenon. These are an extinct group of Eocene and Oligocene hoofed herbivores belonging to the mammalian order Perissodactyla along with the horses, tapirs, and rhinoceroses. Their size increase was relatively rapid, and was spectacular. In the early Eocene they were small, comparable to early horses in size, but in the Oligocene they were elephantine in bulk. In America they became extinct after the early Oligocene, but a few forms survived into the middle Oligocene in Asia. Their whole history was

[15] A more extended discussion of this example, with references to other literature, is given in G. G. Simpson, "Orthogenesis and the Synthetic Theory of Evolution," a paper read in Paris in 1947 and still in press in France when the present book was written. The possible role of relative growth in the gryphaeas was suggested by T. S. Westoll in discussion of this paper at the time of its presentation.

run in the course of perhaps 25,000,000 years or less, while the horse family, which evolved less radically in size but more in most other features, has a history of 60,000,000 years and is still going. The latest titanotheres had, in most cases, large protuberances of the skull bones on the front of the face which look like blunt horns and are commonly called horns, although the chances are that they were covered with calloused skin rather than true horn. The earliest titanotheres had no such protuberances. (See fig. 12.)

It seems quite apparent that these structures were adaptive. They must have been effective battering rams and useful as such to their possessors, whether fighting among themselves or fending off enemies. A skeleton in the American Museum has a broken and later healed rib that could well have resulted from attack by the horns of a fellow titanothere. When horns first appeared, in the later Eocene forms, they arose independently in several different lines and arose gradually, at first as mere thickenings of the skull bones in this region. From this stage they developed into large, fully effective weapons by a rather rapid trend in each line.[16]

Argument that this trend was not oriented by adaptation depends on the assertion that the incipient stages of bone thickening were of no advantage or use to the animals possessing them: the structure starts first, and its usefulness comes later.[17] There are, nevertheless, at least two alternative explanations both of which would make the trend adaptive throughout and either of which or both together are more likely than nonadaptive orientation of the trend. The first consists simply of the counterassertion that the incipient stages were useful. It is likely that the animals had the habit of butting each other and their enemies, even at this stage; they had already become rather stocky, lumbering creatures with stout heads, and they had no other evident means of fighting. Thickening of the bones in the butting region would then be of advantage. The claim that the thickening was not enough to be useful at all or to be effective in orienting further change is not valid in the light of present knowledge. Any thickening would be of some advantage, however slight this might be, and recent studies show that in populations of medium to great abundance any appreciable advantage, even

[16] H. F. Osborn, *The Titanotheres of Ancient Wyoming, Dakota, and Nebraska* (U. S. Geological Survey, Monograph 55 [1929]).

[17] It is probable that this may occasionally happen in the case of some characters developed all at once by mutation. This is a sort of preadaptation and is one of the random, not one of the oriented aspects of evolution. Continued development, a trend, cannot be random throughout, although it may start at random. The question here is not whether a character ever appears prior to its usefulness but whether or not trends are oriented by adaptation. Still another problem concerns the transformation of a character developed with one use so that it comes to serve another.

though exceedingly slight, may be surprisingly effective in producing further change of the same sort in subsequent generations.

There is also evidence that relative growth affected the evolution of horns in titanotheres.[18] The group seems to show a relative growth pattern in which below a certain body size horns do not occur at all, while above this critical size as growth increases the horns increase still more rapidly. Now if this growth pattern were already established before the later Eocene, the smaller animals of those earlier times would not have horns, but horns would appear in any and all lines in which adaptive increase in size passed the critical point. Thereafter development both of horns and of body size would be accelerated because both are advantageous, adaptive trends and the two go together. Thus the whole trend is adaptive from beginning to end. This begs the question, for the present, at least, as to how such a growth pattern arose in the first place, but there is certainly no reason to think it arose by a nonadaptive trend.

The example of the evolution of the horse family has been advanced as typical of a sort of over-all, nonadaptive control of trends. It has been claimed that in the horse family the major trends continue unvaryingly and unchecked regardless of changes in habit or in environmental factors.[19] We have already seen enough of the facts of evolution in this family to suspect that this is not true. Brief further consideration fully confirms the suspicion. There are no really uniform and general trends in the evolution of this family; all trends are to some extent peculiar to one line or another, or effective only at one time or another. The most nearly general trends, such as progression in brain structure, would be useful and adaptive to all horses whatever their precise habits or environments. (In later stages, at least, this also involves correlation with size and a probable relative growth factor.) Increase in size was absent during the Eocene and in some lines at later times, and it was reversed in other lines. Where it does occur is apparently where it was adaptive; its very irregularity negates any over-all trend not adaptive in nature. In other characters, changes in habits or environmental conditions, to the extent that we can infer these from the record,

[18] See A. H. Hersh, "Evolutionary Relative Growth in the Titanotheres" (*Amer. Naturalist*, 68 [1934], 537-561). Later studies of relative growth suggest modification of some of the methods used in this work, but its essential conclusions seem to stand.

[19] For instance, the following product of exceptionally wide but inadequately integrated learning, O. Abel, "Das biologische Trägheitsgesetz" (*Biologia Generalis*, 4 [1928], 1-102).

do definitely involve also changes in the direction of trends. Indeed the whole history of the family seems outstandingly clear in evidence that its trends cannot possibly be explained by control by any factor except adaptation.

All these examples, and many more of the same sort cited by opponents of this view, seem on even this superficial analysis rather to support than to oppose the view that adaptation is the orienting factor in evolutionary trends. At the least, all such trends could possibly have this basis. Still more examples could be given to show that trends stop or change direction when they cease to be advantageous, in other words, when the adaptive control dictates. This happens, indeed, as just mentioned for the horse family, in the very examples often put forward to prove that it does not occur!

Adaptation has a known mechanism: natural selection acting on the genetics of populations. More as to the operation of this mechanism will be said when more has been learned about adaptation and other evolutionary phenomena. It is certainly not thoroughly understood as yet, but its reality is established and its adequacy is highly probable. In seeking the orienting factor in evolution we have seen that in some cases this must, by all reasonable inferences, be adaptation and in all, even the most doubtful, it could be adaptation. Thus we have a choice between a concrete factor with a known mechanism and the vagueness of inherent tendencies, vital urges, or cosmic goals, without known mechanism.

With no pretense at having plumbed the whole mystery or excluded all other possibilities, it is concluded that the major (if not the only) nonrandom, orienting factor in the process of evolution is reasonably identified as adaptation. Some examples have been given and some implications suggested. The enquiry is to be pressed forward into other aspects of the complex phenomena of life.

4. The Opportunism of Evolution

OVER and over again in the study of the history of life it appears that what can happen does happen. There is little suggestion that what occurs *must* occur, that it was fated or that it follows some fixed plan, except simply as the expansion of life follows the opportunities that are presented. In this sense, an outstanding characteristic of evolution is its opportunism. "Opportunism" is, to be sure, a somewhat dangerous word to use in this discussion. It may carry a suggestion of conscious action or of prescience in exploitation of the potentialities of a situation. Language developed (it, too, is a phenomenon of the evolution of life) in a strictly human setting, for communication between the members of mankind. Its words too often carry undertones appropriate to the human scene and misleading in discussion of the grander scene in which men have so late, so brief, and yet so important a part. The present discussion is a communication from one human being to others, so it employs the words already developed for this purpose. It tries to avoid the amiable foible of scientists who are so prone to coin new words for phenomena which should not be viewed in terms of human motives and actions. But when a word such as opportunism is used, the reader should not read into it any personal meaning or anthropomorphic implication. No conscious seizing of opportunities is here meant, nor even an unconscious sensing of an outcome. The word is only a convenient label for these tendencies in evolution: that what can happen usually does happen; changes occur as they may and not as would be hypothetically best; and the course of evolution follows opportunity rather than plan.

What can happen is always limited and often quite strictly limited. Boundless opportunity for evolution has never existed. This has already become apparent in the study of orientation and trends in evolution. Possible ways of life are always restricted in two ways: the environment must offer the opportunity and a group of organisms must have the possibility of seizing this opportunity. On both sides these possibilities have changed greatly in the course of evolution and have, on the whole, become more abundant and more varied. Life, opportunistically, has become more abundant and more varied in accordance with the expansion of these possibilities. Life itself has made the greatest difference in expanding the possibilities of the environment, for each change by one group has opened new opportunities for others: the rise of land plants created the earlier nonexistent opportunity for the development of land animals; the rise of vertebrates provided, in the blood streams of these animals, a new and favorable environment for protozoan life. Purely physical expansions of environmental opportunities have often occurred, too, although many of these have turned out to be temporary. The uprearing of mountain heights provides the opportunity for differentiation of plants and animals adapted to more rarefied atmosphere, more intense solar radiation, more constant cold, and other alpine conditions. The spread and retreat of glaciers or the permutations of climates between warm and cool, moist and arid, seasonal and equable, also provide continually changing opportunities.

On the side of the organisms, each change in them also changes their possibilities for future development, usually limiting them on one side and expanding them on another. Mere geographic position may do this: opportunity for expansion into the sea does not exist for land forms that do not reach the shore; opportunity for alpine expansion may arise for groups that spread into the foothills. Changing structure has still more pervasive and profound effects on limitation and expansion of possibilities. Agglomeration of cells, the origin of multicellular or metazoan structure, put a new lower limit on size and excluded many ways of life followed by the protozoans, but it greatly increased the upper limit on size and it began to open up a new world of opportunities involved in the increasing possibility of tissue and organ differentiation. Increasing development of grasping feet in primates excluded for them any immediate opportunity to match the fleetness of the deer, but it led to opportunities whose seizing eventuated in the finger on a trigger, against which the deer's fleetness is futile.

Within the groups of organisms there are other universally potent controls over what changes can happen in their evolution. They must have the materials for such changes, not only in the sense of established structural norms but also and more particularly in the sense of variations from those norms, of the potientiality for changes in them in order to adapt them to meet new opportunities or necessities. One way in which organisms meet this need is by flexibility in their existing growth patterns and functional systems. Twin seeds from a tree may be planted, one at timberline and another on a watered plain; if the growth pattern common to the two is sufficiently flexible and adaptable, the first will produce a matted shrub well suited to alpine life and the second will produce a tall and slender tree ideally adapted to its more genial situation. An animal whose dental and digestive systems are omnivorous in type may change from one type of food to another, as opportunity presents, without requiring or awaiting an evolutionary change in those systems.

Conversely, a seed from a tree whose growth is rigidly patterned to life on a fertile lowland will not grow if planted on a mountain top, and an animal with teeth and digestive tract adapted strictly for eating meat alone cannot, unless radical structural change intervenes in the evolution of the group, meet a need or exploit an opportunity to live on fruits.

Every group of organisms has its established possibilities in these respects, sometimes a very wide range and sometimes very narrow, but always with limits. A bear may be nourished by ants, fish, chipmunks, raspberries, corn, and a great variety of other foods, but still it cannot survive on leaves or grass. A weasel must have fresh blood and flesh or it soon dies. A cow must have green vegetable food, but almost any sort of leaves or grass permits survival. A koala requires eucalyptus leaves and no others will do.

Of importance still more profound are possibilities and limitations not, like these, inherent in the individual or in the norm of the group but permitting or prohibiting the rise of new kinds of individuals and of new norms. Such developments are the real crux of evolution. (We do not suppose that bears have evolved when they stop fishing and range inland to eat berries, although the ability to do this is an essential factor in bear evolution.) In a larger sense, the development of opportunities in evolution demands changes in the heredity of the given group. Such changes involve three processes: the determinants of heredity, mainly the genes and chromosomes, already present in the group may change in proportions within the population, some perhaps being eliminated, others once rare becoming common; these determinants may be recombined in different ways and so reinforce or modify each other that their result, the growing and adult organism, comes to be of a type not previously present in the population; or new sorts of determinants—mutations—may appear within the population. All three processes are usually going on at the same time in any continuing, reproducing group of organisms and all three are involved in the usual long-range events of evolution.

Opportunities for evolutionary change are thus ultimately both created and limited by what can result from determinants already present in a population of organisms and from mutations among those determinants, which, in fact, are themselves the results of earlier mutations. Opportunities for flying insect eaters existed for millions of years before there were any pterodactyls, birds, or bats to exploit them. The opportunity could not be seized until there were organisms that had the required mutations for development of wings and of the many other related necessities of this way of life. These immediately required mutations themselves had to follow after innumerable others for development of limbs that could become wings, of jaws that could be adapted to seizing insects, and so on through an almost incredibly complex sequence of changes.

Among large numbers of organisms and over long periods

of time such as are involved in the history of life, mutations are exceedingly abundant, but they are also exceedingly erratic. In experimentation, some ways of speeding up their appearance and of slowing it down have been discovered, but no general principle as to their nature or the orientation of their effects has yet been found. We do know one negative fact: the results of mutations do not tend to correspond at all closely with the needs or opportunities of the mutating organisms. It is a rather astonishing observation that the sup-

Fig. 13. Heads of the principal types of antelopes in the Belgian Congo. For discussion, see text. Direct copy from Schouteden.*

* H. Schouteden, "De Zoogdieren van Belgisch-Congo en van Ruanda-Urundi," *An. Mus. Belg. Congo*, C, ser. 2, *3* (1947), fasc. 1-3.

ply of this basic material for evolution seems to have no particular relationship to the demand. This accounts for much of the opportunism in evolution, and the nature of that opportunism in turn attests the random nature of mutation.

Evolution works on the materials at hand: the groups of organisms as they exist at any given time and the mutations that happen to arise in them. The materials are the results of earlier adaptations plus random additions and the orienting factor in change is adaptation to new opportunities. If this view of evolution is correct, then we must expect to find similar opportunities exploited in different ways. The problems involved in performing certain functions should have multiple solutions. As environmental opportunities arise, it should be seen that their development is occasionally delayed or even, rarely, missed altogether, and that when development occurs it may be by a variety of different groups all of which will attain similar adaptations but may do so along different paths and by different means. These expectations are, in fact, abundantly fulfilled in the history of life.

Take, for instance, the expectation of multiple solutions of adaptational problems. These exist for almost any such problem that you can name and they account for much of the swarming diversity of life. The antelopes probably provide an example as good as any among the great number that could be adduced. An essential feature of their adaptation or requirement of their way of life is the development of horns, their principal means of offense in struggles within the groups and of defense against attack from other animals. All the antelopes have horns, but they are not exactly alike in any two species. Even among the antelopes of a single region today, with diversity far less than for the group as a whole in its far-flung history, the differences are quite amazing, as may be seen in figure 13.

Now there must be some one type of horn that would be the most effective possible for antelopes, with some minor variation in proportions or shape in accordance with the sizes or detailed habits of the animals.[1] Obviously not all of these antelopes have the "best" type of horns, and probably none of them has. Why, for instance, with their otherwise

---

[1] There are cases, particularly among birds but also in other groups, where it is advantageous for conspicuous markings or structures to be different among otherwise similar animals, as means of quick recognition by their fellows in the same species. If this were an important factor among antelopes, the horns should be distinctly different among the forms most similar in other respects and so most likely to be mistaken one for the other. Such is not the case; species most similar in other respects are also most similar in the horns. Note, for instance, the two species of reedbuck (*Redunca*), 12 and 14 in the figure, or of sable or roan antelope (*Hippotragus*), 18 and 19. Even if recognition were a factor in the evolution of these horns, the nature of their diversity would still be inexplicable as completely adaptive.

rather close similarity, should the horns of the reedbuck (14 in the figure) curve forward and those of the roan antelope (18) curve backward? Do not the impala (11) and kob (15) horns, with their double curve, seem to achieve the same functional placing and direction as the reedbuck horns (12 and 14) with a single curve, but to do so in a way mechanically weaker? Even though the animals themselves are small, are not the duiker horns (9 and 10) too small to be really effective, and are not the tremendous kudu horns (23) unnecessarily unwieldy?

If evolution were really operating according to a fixed plan, surely these radical discrepancies would not arise. Nor would they arise if evolution were basically orthogenetic or if a rigid orientation were everywhere the rule. It looks as if there had been an orienting factor, indeed—all these animals do have horns that serve them well enough even if not perfectly—but as if what it had to orient was not uniform or completely responsive. As horns developed in the different lines different sorts of mutations affected them. As long as the mutations increased the development of a functional horn, however various in other respects, they served the adaptive end and were retained and promoted in the evolution of each line. The mutations that would have been mechanically the best, that an engineer would have chosen, simply did not happen to occur in all, or perhaps in any, of these lines. There are two aspects of opportunism: to seize such diverse opportunities as occur, and when a single opportunity or need occurs, to meet it with what is available, even if this is not the best possible. The antelopes, and many other groups of animals, well illustrate this second sort of evolutionary opportunism.

Examples like this have, oddly enough, been used to argue that horns (or whatever feature it may be) are not adaptive and that their usefulness, if any, is sheer accident. It is claimed that adaptive control should mean the reaching of a single solution for each functional problem. This quite overlooks the established fact that adaptation can only orient changes that really do arise in animals and that these are guided but not evoked by adaptation. It is only under vitalist and finalist theories that one can suppose that the changes that arise are indeed just the ones needed for best adaptation —and examples such as that of the antelopes add their weight to the great bulk of evidence making those theories untenable. On the other hand, if under the claimed alternative there were no orientation whatever and horns developed quite by chance, then surely some would be merely fantastic and would not work at all. They all do function sufficiently well, some better and some worse but all well enough to serve. It really seems as if the explanation given here were the only one that is reasonable.

Another example is worthy of some discussion not only because it reinforces the conclusion suggested by antelope horns but also because it has an important bearing on some other important evolutionary principles. This is the nature and evolution of photoreceptors among animals. In a great many animals, invertebrate and vertebrate, it is clearly advantageous to have some means of receiving and consequently of responding to the stimulus of light. In some animals this may be of no particular value and in a few it may be downright disadvantageous, but it is a characteristic useful in a particularly wide variety of environments and of ways of life. Apparatuses for receiving light stimulus, photoreceptors, have correspondingly developed in a great number of widely different sorts of animals. Some photoreceptors merely give the information that light is present, or absent. Others give, sometimes with great accuracy, information as to the direction from which light is coming or as to the relative intensities of light from different directions. Still others form an image and give information about the shape of the particular object that is emitting or reflecting the light received. They may even add information as to how far away the object is, how fast it is moving, and what wave lengths of light (colors) it emits or reflects. Our own eyes do these things and are among the most versatile and effective ever evolved, although there are many animals with eyes that excel ours in some particular or another.[2]

The function of receiving light stimuli is highly special and definite in its requirements. It might be supposed that there was just one way to develop this function, or at least that there was one best way leading at last to an apparatus capable of receiving all the information that light can convey. In fact the variety of photoreceptors among animals is almost incredible. Given the properties of animal cells and tissues in general, it seems nearly impossible to think of a practical means of photoreception that has not appeared in one group or another, or in more than one. (For a very few examples, see figures 14-15.) And yet the theoretical best or the perfect eye has never been achieved. All fall decidedly short of the ability to gather all the information that light

[2] One of the most useful discussions of photoreceptors in general is in L. Plate's *Allgemeine Zoologie und Abstammungslehre*, Teil II: "Die Sinnesorgane der Tiere" (Jena, G. Fischer, 1924). A truly fascinating account of the structure and history of the particular sort of image-forming eye that arose early in vertebrate evolution is given by G. L. Walls, *The Vertebrate Eye and Its Adaptive Radiation* (Bloomfield Hills, Michigan, Cranbrook Institute of Science, 1942).

can convey. The best of them have had to compromise, sacrificing one sort of information for better reception of another.

In some protozoans the body, undivided into separate cells, is light-sensitive as a whole. In others a special photosensitive spot (stigma) is developed within the protoplasm.

Fig. 14. Some light-receiving organs or photoreceptors. 1, a single-celled or noncellular protozoan (*Pouchetia*) with a light sensitive pigment-spot (stigma) and lenslike denser region. 2, section through skin of an earthworm with two of the scattered light-sensitive cells. 3, sections through three types of photoreceptors in starfish: A, sensitive cells grouped in a flat plate; B, cells infolded to form a basin; C, basin with rudimentary lens. 4, section through photoreceptor of a flatworm, with ends of sensitive cells pointing into a pigmented basin. 5, sections through three types of eyes in gastropods (snails, etc.): A, a simple basin; B, deep retinal basin filled with lenslike secretion; C, well-developed spherical eye with retina and lens. 6, section through the highly differentiated eye of a clam.

Some of these forms also have a lenslike mass of high refractive index that concentrates light on the sensitive spot. These types seem to exhaust the possibilities without cell and organ differentiation. More numerous and complex types of photoreceptors appear among the multicelled animals. Special photosensory cells may be scattered over or in the body. These may be gathered in groups, which may vary greatly in size, number, shape, and position. More distinctly defined groups of these photosensory cells may form flat plates, grooves, basins, or bubblelike vesicles. They may be turned toward the incoming light, away from it, or at an angle to it.

The sensory cells may be few or exceedingly many and may or may not be backed by a special layer of pigmented cells, which may themselves be of most various forms. All these types and combinations may be accompanied by a light-concentrating lens (again with a variety of shapes and structures), or may lack this. Moreover, similar parts of the apparatus may arise in different ways in different groups.

Fig. 15. Continuation of fig. 14, some advanced types of image-forming eyes. 7, section through the eye of a cuttlefish, functionally like the eyes of vertebrates but developed differently. 8, section through the eye of a vertebrate (man). 9, section through the pinhole eye of the chambered nautilus. 10, section and partial perspective of the multiple-tube (compound) eye of an insect (diagrammatic, only). Figs. 14-15 have been redrawn from numerous sources, data mostly as compiled by Plate after Hesse and others.)

Image-forming eyes,[3] which gather information not only about incoming light but also about the objects from which it comes, are also of various types but are confined to animals of considerable anatomical complexity and are themselves relatively complex photoreceptors. Aside from the fact that image formation is complicated and requires a large number of highly differentiated parts to function properly, it requires also some complexity of other functional parts of

---

[3] Some students call these "iconogenetic," but the term is no shorter than "image-forming" and means exactly the same thing to fewer people.

the organism if the image so formed is to be of any particular use. If a protozoan were to receive an image by its sensory apparatus it is, so to speak, difficult to see what it could do about this; the protozoan lacks sufficiently complex systems to discriminate one sort of image from another or to modify its behavior accordingly, nor is it conceivable that such complexity could be developed within a single mass of protoplasm. Similarly among other animals, when photoreceptor evolution stopped short of image formation it seems likely, at least, in most cases that this was because it had gone about as far as was really useful (or adaptive) for the particular sort of animal, with its general structural level and way of life.

Image-forming eyes are by no means uniform, even as regards the general optical principles on which they operate. There are optically four ways in which images can be formed: lens, pinhole, multiple tubes, and concave reflector. The first three are all found in image-forming eyes of various animals, the lens, for instance, in you, the pinhole in the chambered nautilus, and the multiple tubes in flies. The reflector principle does not seem to have been used in any image-forming eye unless, just possibly, in some extinct type. It is, in fact, improbable that animal anatomy and tissues could have met minimum requirements for efficient use of the reflector principle.[4] The lens and pinhole principles are familiar enough to photographers and most others. They may operate simultaneously, as when a camera diaphragm is stopped down, and this combination is also common among image-forming eyes. (The iris is the diaphragm in the eye; its contraction stops down the opening and increases depth and sharpness of focus —in some animals with lens eyes going so far as essentially to take over the image-forming function from the lens.) Multiple tubes operate on the principle that since light travels in straight lines, only light from straight in front of each tube will traverse it and come out the other end. If each tube of a large bundle is pointed straight at a different part of the object, each will transmit light from that part only, and place it in a mosaic that is, at least roughly, an image of the object. The system would not be flexible or efficient for photography but it is employed, and highly developed, in the compound eyes of insects.

Lenses arose in evolution as light-gathering or -concentrating rather than as image-forming apparatuses. Since they can, in fact, create images as well as gather light (and, inci-

---

[4] Retina and pigment cup or disc would have to be reversed with respect to incoming light and interposed in its path without cutting it off, while an efficient internal reflector would have to develop. Such a development might not be quite impossible but it seems very nearly so.

dentally, pinholes and multiple tubes cannot gather light), it is not surprising that they were most often involved in further evolution to image-forming eyes. In the evolution of compound eyes they were retained but did not change function: in the insect eye each tube has a lens which serves to concentrate and direct light, not to form an image. In molluscs and in the vertebrates, two groups with optically advanced image-forming eyes, the lens usually became the image former.

The remarkable similarity between the eyes of an octopus (which is a mollusc) and of a man has been cited as evidence of the existence of a uniform plan in evolution, of some over-all life force or final aim. Yet we have seen that these are only selected examples among a great array of photoreceptors which include almost every conceivable sort. And also, hidden in these eyes there is an evolutionary joker which is evidence, too: they work in almost exactly the same way, but they do not develop and did not evolve in the same way. In the vertebrate eye the retina or rather its sensory cells are aimed away from the light and in molluscs they are aimed toward it. The same remarkable difference is found in some non-image-forming eyes among invertebrates. Evolution has been opportunistic again: among its myriad solutions of the problem of photoreception are two in which the solution in principle is almost identical but in which, as usual, it did only the best possible from the materials at hand. Those materials happened to be different in the two cases so that actual identity could not be achieved.

The evolution of the eye is frequently cited in opposition to the sort of conclusions here drawn by two schools of evolutionists who, aside from this, may have little in common. Their contention is not entirely pertinent to the present chapter, but it is desirable to mention it briefly here while the example is before us. Both schools submit that the image-forming eye could not function until *after* it was complete. From this statement the two draw radically different conclusions. One group, the finalists, concludes that therefore the eye evolved with reference to a *future* function, that the structure began first and use for it came only millions of years later when it was fully evolved and could begin to fulfill the purpose for which it was destined from the start. The other group unites, on this point, such odd bedfellows as the antievolutionists or special creationists and certain evolutionists who disbelieve in adaptive control of evolution and believe instead in catastrophically sudden changes of structure —what one of them, Schindewolf, calls "typostrophism." These agree that since the image-forming eye, so they say, could not function until complete, therefore it became complete all at once. It did not slowly change to its present state through the ages but arose as it now is in one bang, created so by God or by Mutation—or Typostrophism.

Inadequate as it is, the preceding discussion of photoreceptors sufficiently points up the fallacy of these contentions. If all photoreceptors except the image-forming eyes of advanced molluscs and of vertebrates had become extinct, there would be an excuse for bewilderment. In fact, representative stages at every gradually different level happen to have survived, from diffuse photosensitivity of the whole body through scattered photosensitive cells to cell plates, basins, basins and vesicles plus lenses, and so on to the fully developed image-forming eye with lens, iris, and its other complexities. These photoreceptors function splendidly at every level and do not wait to start working until the final stage is reached. They simply enlarge, refine, and to some extent change their functions as they become more complex.

To return to more direct discussion of the opportunistic nature of evolution, this is still more widely apparent in such phenomena as divergence and adaptive radiation or convergence and analogous change from different origins. Adaptive radiation represents the exploitation of possible ways of life by the groups of organisms that happen to be present at the same time and place where the opportunities occur and by means of mutations in the characteristics that they happen already to have. In Chapter 1 of this book it has already been seen how major, and also minor, groups of animals start with some basic adaptive type, the descendants of which then tend to diverge and to take on a wide variety of habits. It should be emphasized that the basic type is itself specifically adapted to a particular way of life. It does not broadly include all the ways later followed by its descendants, nor does it simply embody the general features that these may all have in common. As Romer has so well remarked, you cannot make a living by being generalized.

The basic placental mammal, for instance, occupied a particular niche in the ecology of its time. It was an active, tiny, quadrupedal type of animal, with its obscurity as main defense, eating mainly small animal food such as worms or insects and their larvae, but probably also somewhat omnivorous and able to supplement its diet with some of the more nutritious plant foods, small fruits and the like. From this basis, evolution opportunistically developed extremely diverse types. Some mammals continued to follow the ancestral way of life but became more highly and rigidly adapted to it and parceled out its various specialties among different lines. These are the living insectivores. Some became aerial (bats) and some aquatic (whales, and others). Some became herbivorous (most hoofed mammals, most rodents, and some others) and some carnivorous (most carnivores and some others). Each category can be repeatedly subdivided: the diversity includes hundreds of distinct adaptive types. Thus among the many sorts of herbivores some are terrestrial, some subterranean, some arboreal, some aerial, some aquatic. Among terrestrial herbivores some browse, some graze, some eat fruits, and so on. Among terrestrial grazers, some are small, some large; some are fleet, some ponderous. It seems as if no possibility had been skipped.

The essentially opportunistic nature of this process is particularly evident when, as has repeatedly happened, the same sorts of opportunities have occurred for different groups of animals. An often-repeated example is that of the marsupials as compared with the placentals. It happens that of these two major subdivisions arising among early (Cretaceous) mammals, only the marsupials soon reached Australia, then as now an island.[5] Within Australia from this marsupial stock developed a radiation that came to include most of the important adaptive types that arose elsewhere by radiation of the placental mammals. There are insectivorelike marsupials (for example, the so-called marsupial anteater, *Myrmecobius*), molelike marsupials (the pouched "mole," *Notoryctes*), doglike marsupials (the Tasmanian "wolf," *Thylacinus*), squirrellike marsupials (the phalangers, subfamily Phalangerinae, including even marsupial "flying squirrels," the flying "opossums" or gliders of the Australians, *Acrobates* and *Petaurus*) —and so on, through many more types. The variety is not as great as among the placentals, but the opportunities offered by Australia were obviously not as extensive or varied as those offered by all the other continents put together.

South America, also an island during most of the Tertiary, provides an even more extensive example, complicated by the fact that its original mammalian stocks were more varied than those of Australia and included both marsupials and placentals. Lengthy discussion is not necessary, but a few of the products of this radiation may be compared in figure 16 and in tabular form with those of North American radia-

[5] Some geologists deny that Australia was an island when mammals spread to it, and the whole history is sometimes interpreted quite differently. There is, nevertheless, excellent and, I think, adequate reason for the views here briefly suggested. Other complications are introduced by the fact that sometime during the Tertiary two types of placental mammals did gain access to Australia and became abundant there: the Old World rats and the bats. In the Pleistocene came man and the dog (dingo). This is not the place to consider the whole very large problem of the history of the Australian fauna. The differences of opinion and the complication do not really matter here, anyway, because there is general agreement on the main point of analogous radiations among marsupials and placentals.

tion, which was also connected and involved with Eurasia and Africa at various times:

SOUTH AMERICA		NORTH AMERICA	
General stock	Special types	Special types	General stock
Marsupialia	Caenolestines	Shrews	Insectivora
	Polydolopids	Squirrels or mice	Rodentia
	Borhyaenines	Dogs	Carnivora
	Thylacosmilus	Sabertooths	
Pyrotheria	Pyrotheres	Mastodonts	Proboscidea
Litopterna	Macraucheniines	Camels	Artiodactyla
	Proterotheres	Horses	
Notoungulata	Toxodonts	Rhinoceroses	Perissodactyla
	Homalodotheres	Chalicotheres	

That such phenomena represent opportunism and not plan or purpose in evolution is attested by the fact that such independent radiations produce animals similar in way of life but not the same in structure, indeed sometimes remarkably different. The kangaroos of Australia (along with a few extinct types such as *Diprotodon*) are analogous to the hoofed herbivores of the rest of the world and have exploited some of the same opportunities as far as these existed in Australia—but how obviously different they are! The Tasmanian "wolf" or thylacine, at the other extreme, does look almost like a dog of sorts at first sight, and yet it would be a stupid anatomist who could not distinguish the two from any single bone or organ in the body. Similarly in South America the extinct macraucheniines may have looked only vaguely like camels but must have had rather similar ways of life. Some of the extinct proterotheres must have looked extraordinarily like some horses, but, as in the case of the thylacine and dog, no single tooth or bone of a proterothere is really exactly like that of any horse. The radiations produced similar results because they represent the development of similar opportunities. They did not produce the same results because they were opportunistic. The opportunities were seized not in the hypothetically most effective ways, not in uniform ways, not, in short, according to plan, but as best they might be, departing from groups already distinctive in character and developing by selection of random mutations which were not the same in the different stocks and not precisely what was needed for mechanical perfection.

Similar phenomena are seen when the evolution of particular organs or structures, rather than that of organisms as a whole, is considered. For instance the basic forelimb of the land vertebrates, five-toed and adapted for walking, has undergone remarkable radiations among later animals. Among other things, it has become a one-toed, tip-toe running apparatus (in proterotheres and horses), an arm and hand (in you

Fig. 16. Some convergent types among North and South American mammals, mostly extinct forms. All are drawn to the same scale.

and me), a webbed paddle (in duck-bill dinosaurs, otters and others), a flipper (in ichthyosaurs, whales, etc.), a wing (in pterodactyls, birds, and bats), and so on. Again recurrent development of the same opportunity is found, and again the opportunism is made evident by similarity without identity and by multiple solutions for the same problems. Throughout, the limb remains essentially the same. It was developed into all these different forms departing from an ancestral type common to all. The forelimb is thus said to be *homologous* among all these vertebrates in spite of such striking differences in structure and function. This common basis and homology have not prevented multiple solutions as an opportunity was seized at different times, by groups with somewhat different forelimbs and with different random mutations. Wings, for instance, have developed three times from terrestrial forelimbs (see fig. 17), in the reptilian pterodactyls, in the birds, and in the mammalian bats. In each case the same functional problem, in each case a solution achieving the same end, but in each case a decidedly different structural way of developing a wing.

This sort of opportunistic development of multiple solutions is even more striking when the element of an ultimate ancestral structure in common is lacking. Then the structures developed for the function in question are not homologous but only analogous. Their differences are commonly more radical than in the case, for instance, of the homologous bird and bat wings, and yet essentially identical functions may be served. Insect wings (fig. 17), as compared with the wings of flying vertebrates, are a good example.

The development of the same sort of evolutionary opportunity by different groups of organisms produces the evolutionary phenomena known as parallelism and convergence. There is no really fundamental difference between these two. In parallelism, groups already adaptively and structurally similar independently undergo changes in the same direction (involved in seizing the same sort of opportunity for a modified way of life). They thus both change and yet continue to be about equally similar. Such groups are likely to be rather closely related to begin with and to have not only a structurally similar basis on which change occurs but also rather similar mutations as a means of change. Mutations, like structures, are likely to be more nearly alike in closely than in distantly related animals. It is not surprising that this process may produce forms that are almost, although perhaps never precisely, identical. The gryphaeas, mentioned in discussing oriented evolution, are a good example. They represent several parallel developments from the same continuing oyster stock (*Ostrea*). The end results are in each case so similar that they are commonly considered as collectively forming a single group, *Gryphaea*, although they can be distinguished and do have separate origins within *Ostrea*.

In convergence, there occurs the same sort of opportunistic development of one way of life (or closely similar ways) by different groups, but in this case those groups are dissimilar (or less similar) in adaptive type to start with. Trend toward greater similarity of adaptation involves increasing or con-

Fig. 17. Different sorts of wings. Pterodactyl (flying reptile), bird, and bat wings developed independently from the forefeet of land-living vertebrates: the bones in them are (largely) homologous; the wings as such and their functions are analogous. The insect wing has a totally different origin: it is analogous only to the other wings shown.

verging functional and structural characteristics. The groups
may be nearly related or may be only very distantly related.
Especially among more nearly related groups, the convergence
is likely to involve homologous structures, as is also true
of parallelism. Homologous structures, having similarities due
to common origin, are likely, in opportunistic fashion, to
lend themselves to modification for serving similar new functions. On the other hand, among distantly related groups
such homologous structures are less likely to be present and
convergence may affect organs developed completely independently in each group. The convergent wings of pterodactyls,
birds and bats arise from homologous forelimbs, although
they do not arise in the same way. Insects and birds are so
distantly related that any particular homology between their
parts can hardly be traced, and yet they may converge, sometimes quite closely. Humming moths and humming birds are
so remarkably alike in habits and functional operation that
they are often mistaken for each other if seen only from a
distance.

Convergence on a grand scale is seen in the comparison
of South and North American mammals. The "special types"
placed opposite each other in the preceding tabulation are in
each case convergent. Here, too, is seen the quite general

Fig. 18. Relationships between divergence and convergence in
adaptive evolution.

fact that convergence results from divergence, an apparent paradox that is resolved when the opportunism of evolution is taken into account. Divergence within a group involves the seizing of various different evolutionary opportunities. Another group may diverge in a way involving some of the same opportunities. Members of the two groups diverging in ways involving the same opportunity converge toward each other.[6] (See fig. 18.)

This review of some of the opportunistic elements in evolution reinforces the evidence, seen also in discussing oriented evolution, that evolution is neither wholly orderly nor wholly disorderly. It certainly has no grand and uniform plan, nor any steady progression toward a discernible goal. On the other hand, it shows continued trends and a neat interlocking of the various sorts of organisms so that they interact systematically and fill out the possible ways of life, many of which they have themselves, by merely coming into being, created. The history of life is an odd blend of the directed and the random, the systematic and the unsystematic.

As a final remark on this topic, it is to be noted that evolution is not completely systematic even in its opportunism. Apparent opportunities are not always exploited and gaps are not invariably soon filled. The rule that all of life's opportunities tend to be followed up also has exceptions. The extinction of the dinosaurs long preceded the reoccupation of most of their ways of life by the mammals—and not quite all seem yet to have been reoccupied. Ichthyosaurs had been extinct for many millions of years before dolphins and their kin seized this opportunity. There is no evident reason why the way of life of the once so abundant ammonites, extinct marine molluscs related to the chambered nautilus, could not be followed now by equally abundant groups for which the seas may be searched in vain. Many types have become extinct and left open a way of life, an opportunity which could not immediately be seized because no other group had yet a structural basis and a supply of mutations appropriate for the change.

Why, then, the extinction? Here we touch on mysteries of life and death, not of individuals but of whole populations, which must also have some special discussion.

---

[6] For two different recent points of view on this and related subjects, with references to much other literature, see the following papers—which are unfortunately technical and rather difficult: O. Haas, and G. G. Simpson, "Analysis of Some Phylogenetic Terms with Attempts at Redefinition" (*Proc. Amer. Phil. Soc.*, 90 [1946], 319-347); O. H. Schindewolf, " 'Konvergenzen' bei Korallen und bei Ammoneen" (*Fortschr. Geol. Pal.*, 12 [1940], 389-492).

5. Racial Life and Death

RACES are born, rise to a period of maximum development, decline, and die. So do individuals. The parallel is tempting. It can be, and often is, carried further, so that one may speak of "racial youth," "racial maturity," or "racial old age." Even "racial adolescence" may be mentioned, and here the parallel should begin to give pause. Adolescence is the period of maturing during which sexual fertility begins and body growth is essentially completed. Surely races have no period when they become sexually fertile; if not fertile from birth they could never mature. We are in danger here of pushing the analogy too far. Instead of using it only as a sort of metaphor to describe one phenomenon in terms of another quite distinct phenomenon, we have been in danger of assuming that the two phenomena really are the same sort of thing and that we can find in one an equivalent of all the features of the other. That is the trouble with analogies; we may come to think that they will help us to interpret and explain phenomena which, in fact, they can only help, imperfectly and unrealistically, to describe. This confusion has entered into several of the sciences and perhaps most insidiously into the life sciences.[1] Evidently we should not assume that races, because they become old, also become senile, or that when they are young they are virile.

Each normal individual organism has a life pattern which is characteristic of its species and which it follows without strong deviation, barring accident or pathology. Growth continues for a typical period of time to a typical size as limit. Sexual fertility begins at a characteristic time, continues over a period variable within rather definite limits, and then ceases. Degeneration begins to get the upper hand at some time during the period of maturity and leads to decline, senility, and inevitable death. The potential span of life seems to be very rigidly set by the nature of the organism. All the great strides of medicine do not seem to have raised the potential life span of man by one minute; they have only made it possible for more men to come nearer to realizing their potential spans without being cut off earlier by disease or by avoidably rapid degeneration.

[1] One of the most pernicious is the analogy between organism and society. Some further reference to this will later be necessary.

Contrary to an opinion commonly expressed, races, or groups of organisms in general, do not seem to have any such life pattern which appears as a common element in their histories. Still less do they seem to have an inherent growth pattern or metabolic system which brings them to maturity at definite times and which dooms them to death from the internal ravages of old age, even if violence and disease have passed them by. How extremely varied their life histories may be is glimpsed in such selected records as those of figures 2 and 3. Most of them do have in common a period of exceptionally high over-all evolutionary activity of various sorts and one, usually near the same time, when they are particularly widespread, varied, abundant, or successful. It is, however, true that in various groups these periods do not tend to correspond, that they may come early, middle, or late in the history of the group, that they may be long or short, and that they may be single or multiple. The regularity implicit in the evolutionary "Epacme," "Acme," and "Paracme" of Haeckel, the "Typogenese," "Typostase," and "Typolyse" of Schindewolf, the racial "youth," "maturity," and "old age" of many other writers, simply does not exist in this broad picture.

The periods of exceptional evolutionary activity which appear so generally but so irregularly in the histories of groups of organisms are usually ushered in by times of rapid expansion and adaptive radiation, and in most cases they finally taper off with the elimination of many lines of descent and the rather sharp differentiation and narrow adaptive specialization or channeling of the remainder. There is this much regularity and its phases may be likened to "racial youth" and "racial maturity" if you like and if you are not bothered by the fact that "racial youth" may come late, as well as early, in racial life and may occur more than once. In themselves these inconsistencies show that we are not here dealing with any inherent life pattern such as rules the periods of individual life.

The times of rapid expansion, high variability, and beginning adaptive radiation are the "explosive phases" of evolution, to use an infelicitous phrase that seems unfortunately to be deeply established in evolutionary terminology.[2] From what has already been said, it is possible now to interpret these without much further discussion. They are periods when enlarged opportunities are presented to groups able to pursue them.

[2] Cloud has suggested "eruptive evolution," which is perhaps preferable but not completely satisfying, and Rensch suggests *Virenzperioden*, which would be excellent were it not subject to possible confusion in the individual life analogy.

The opportunities may arise when progress of the group itself brings it to the threshold of a new career: the reptiles evolved to the point of independence from water as a living medium and immediately—as such things go in the earth's slow history—burst into a Virenzperiod (in the Permian) in landscapes earlier barren of vertebrate life. Opportunity may come as an inheritance from the dead, the extinct, who bequeath adaptive zones free of competitors: Jurassic Virenz for ammonites followed extinction of all but one family, perhaps all but one genus, of Triassic ammonites; early Tertiary mammalian Virenz followed mysterious decimation of the Cretaceous reptiles. Expansion of one group of organisms may mean multiple opportunities for another: spread and diversification of land plants brought on "explosive" evolution of insects and other land animals. Geographic shifts may bring the opportunity of new lands to exploit: precarious island hopping to Australia gave the marsupials a whole continent to occupy.[3]

A quieter period ensues when the basic radiation has been completed, when, so to speak, the opportunities have been parceled out and each has been claimed by some line of populations descending from the expanding group. Lessened activity here betokens not failure or decline but the prosperous enjoyment of a completed conquest. Change continues but mainly in two ways: the sharpening and increasing adaptation to the way of life embarked upon, and response to changes made necessary in that way of life as time goes on—for no environment is absolutely static. Eliminated lines from the original radiation consist, as a rule, of those so nearly like the surviving lines that they would be in competition with them; these are the *fehlgeschlagenen Anpassungen* of Abel. This, too, is an aspect of the principle of multiple solutions in evolution, discussed from another point of view in the last chapter. In their early phases, adaptive radiations often produce multiple solutions which are simultaneous or closely successive and which occur among animals that are, or come to be, associated with each other. Then one solution may pragmatically prove to be superior to the others, as its possessors displace the rest. Thus in the first radiation of the mammalian carnivores, multiple solutions of the problem of developing flesh-shearing teeth occurred. (Paleocene and Eocene creodonts). One finally became universal (that of the Miacidae and the fissipeds derived from them) and its possessors later expanded and by their own radiation displaced all other carnivores. (See figure 19.)

[3] The contemporaneous record of this "explosion" has not been found, but its results leave no doubt that it occurred.

Wolf

p4

Hyaenodon

m2

m1

Oxyaena

Fig. 19. Divergent, opportunistic formation of flesh-cutting (carnassial) teeth in carnivores. All serve the same function, but different teeth in the series are involved. All occur in the early Tertiary radiation of carnivores, but the type still present in the wolf was most successful and is the only one in living carnivores. (Modified from Matthew.)

The discussion has been simplified and generalized, but it may suffice to show that these phenomena of racial life history need not involve any mysterious or inherent forces and that they fit well into the general ideas of the evolutionary

Fig. 20. Some of the "immortals": a few of the living animals, evolution of which has been practically at a standstill for tens of millions of years.

process that are being developed here. The last phase of life, that of its end in death, is still more important for the problem of the meaning of the history of life, and its study has greater difficulties and uncertainties.

Is extinction the fated end of all groups of organisms, as death is of each individual organism?[4] There are in the world today a large number of types of organisms that arose so long ago that the great majority of their early contemporaries have long been extinct. Some have, indeed, changed enough so that zoologists can apply different specific or generic names to the ancient and recent forms, but in the cases here considered these changes are trivial and represent no essential difference. Among these Methuselahs (see fig. 20) are some already mentioned such as *Sphenodon* (surviving almost unchanged from Jurassic to Recent) or the opossum (Cretaceous to Recent). The invertebrates, older to begin with and generally slower in evolution, provide still more striking examples. The little sea shell *Lingula* is amazingly like its Ordovician ancestor of 400,000,000 years or so ago, and an oyster of 200,000,000 years or more in the past would look perfectly familiar if served in a restaurant today. (There is, indeed, one whole group of animals, the silica-secreting protozoans or Radiolaria, which are claimed to have existed since the preCambrian without one type ever becoming extinct! The case is, however, special on several counts and not entirely comparable with more moderate and yet remarkable records like those just cited.)

If there is a secret of racial immortality, these animals certainly must possess it. The essentials of the secret are not really very esoteric: when it arose each of these animals was well adapted to a particular way of life which has ever since continued to be possible and the requirements for which have never changed. Some of the offspring of these immortals have embarked on ways of life which did disappear or the requirements for which did change, and these branches have become extinct while the parent stock lived on. From the opossums arose the extinct carnivorous marsupials of South America and from the oysters arose the extinct gryphaeas.

Within these broad conditions are others that do make the problem considerably more complex and not yet fully understood. All environments have undergone some changes, however slight, and the immortals must have met these without need for changing themselves. Mutations away from the

---

[4] Discussion of the problem of individuality and of the "immortality" of the ameba, which reproduces by fission, would here be a tempting bypath, but it seems hardly necessary to follow it. Let us agree, in order not to linger over nonessentials, that the ameba as an indivdual dies when it divides and that the two offspring are new individuals.

original and surviving type have certainly occurred, even with frequency, and these must have been rapidly and surely eliminated by special combinations of factors in the interplay of population and environment.

There are some general features common to many, at least, of the immortals and related in some way to such special requirements for survival. Most of them are relatively small animals; large animals make extra demands on space and on food which may not be met during all fluctuations of the environment. Most of them have rather large local populations where they do occur; small populations are especially liable to accidental elimination and also to chance effects of random mutations away from the established type. Most of them have some latitude in adaptation and are not rigidly restricted to one variety of food or to a very narrow environmental range; such restriction may be fatal when casual fluctuations in the environment occur. Most of them live in conditions which are not extreme or unusual as to climate, vegetation, and other environmental factors: in the relatively constant waters of the sea, in temperate forests, and so on, rather than in the Arctic, in deserts, on high mountain peaks, or in other extreme environments. The environments of the immortals are, as a rule, those of longest, most continuous existence. Most of them were progressive animals when they arose and had then evolved rapidly into new adaptive types; they were the first to seize opportunities as they arose and they adapted so well to these that later types did not displace them.

The fact that extinction has not occurred for these animals during their exceptionally long histories does not permit the conclusion that their extinction never will occur and that they are, in literal fact, immortal. Since the Cambrian, at least, and probably long before, no extreme or permanent physical change has affected the earth. Some sorts of environments in the Cambrian and others developing since then have persisted without essential change. Continuity of basic physical conditions may persist for many millions of years or may end tomorrow. It is incredible that it should really continue forever. The sun's energy is finite and must someday reach an end and with it life on the earth must cease. Collision with other celestial bodies, extremely improbable in such limited time as man conceives, is eventually probable in the endless time of "forever." Man himself seems terrifyingly near the knowledge of how to destroy his planet in a blazing chain reaction, and terrifyingly far from the self-control necessary to avoid using this knowledge.

It must be concluded that material racial immortality

is impossible. The time will come when all life ends.[5]

Even though extinction is certain for every form of life, the forms we have been discussing have a sort of conditional immortality, which has carried them up to now and which may well continue as long as life on the earth remains possible under conditions not too unlike those of the last billion years or so. Such ability to survive is exceptional. The vast majority of all the multitudes of minor sorts of organisms that have appeared in the history of life have either changed to forms distinctly different or have disappeared absolutely, without descendants.

Among racial life spans, every range has existed from types that arose hundreds of millions of years ago and are still going strong down to types whose geologically brief moment is no more than a hundred thousand years or so. The differentiation of a distinctly new type of organism normally takes time on the order of hundreds of thousands of years, at least, so that much shorter life spans for such types are not possible. Within any given group of organisms the span of survival for its various sorts or subtypes is extremely variable. The whole range, from the kind of conditional immortality discussed above down to a minimum, may occur in a single group, as it does, for instance, in the pelecypods or bivalves, the clams and their host of allies. Yet within each group there seems to be an average span of racial life which is characteristic for that group and which differs from one group to another. Thus the genera of mammalian land carnivores that have become extinct lasted, on an average, for a period on the order of 8,000,000 years, although some endured for 20,000,000 years, more or less (middle Miocene to Pleistocene), and others disappeared almost as soon as they arose. Extinct pelecypod genera[6] had an average span on the order of nearly 80,000,000 years, about ten times as long as that of the carnivores. Some lasted more than 200,000,000 years before becoming extinct and others again were barely differentiated before they disappeared. Note that the maximum span—for genera that did become extinct; the "immortals" are excluded—is about ten times that for carnivores, as is the average span, and that in each case the maximum is about 2.5 times the average.[7] It is also characteristic of each of these groups, and probably of most other groups of organisms, that short life spans are much more common than long: the great

---

[5] The fantasy of transfer to other planets is not impossible although it is hardly imminent. This might postpone but could not avoid the inevitable end.

[6] Genera construed broadly and not the extremely split genera of some recent classifiers.

[7] The figures are taken, with some modification, from my *Tempo and Mode in Evolution*, previously cited.

majority of genera became extinct after lengths of time nearer the minimum than the maximum for the group as a whole. Extremely short spans, those quite close to a minimum, are, however, less common than those of somewhat greater duration. Most genera tend to have about the same period of survival, characteristic for each group, and those with very short or with moderately to very long relative durations are less common.

There is, then, a rule of extinction for various groups of organisms, and while the figures differ greatly from one group to another there are regularities common to some at least of these groups. Although we failed to find good evidence of a widespread racial life cycle pattern, here is a suggestion of such a pattern for death. The pattern is real, but a little further study of its causes and meaning shows that it is not inherent in the organisms alone, not a fate implanted within the racial tissues as inevitable old age and death are implanted in the tissues of individuals, but is again a phenomenon explicable only on the basis of the complex material interaction of populations and their environments.

For one thing, the pelecypods include a considerable number of the "immortals," and the carnivores include none (so far as we can judge without knowing their future). Some pelecypods still living have been in existence twice as long as the maximum for those that did become extinct. No living genus of carnivores is as old as the maximum span for extinct genera in this group. The pelecypods have available environments within the sea which have undergone no great change through hundreds of millions of years. Some of them have been able to seize this opportunity for indefinitely prolonged survival. Environments available to the land carnivores have changed much more rapidly and more radically. Correspondingly, they have had shorter spans and no opportunities for indefinite continuance of any one type. Aside from these differences, pelecypods have coped, or failed to cope, with the slower changes of the sea and carnivores with the faster changes of the land in accordance with the same principles of adaptation and organic stability and modification.

The figures for extinction have included two different things. If an evolving population of organisms changes so much that it becomes something distinctly different, to be given a different name and considered something new, then the old, ancestral type is gone, extinct, and yet it also lives on in altered form. Extinction in this sense merely reflects the rate of progressive change. A short life span for any one type means not that death soon overtook it but that life rapidly carried it on to other forms of being. Total figures for extinction, such as those given for pelecypods and carnivores, include many cases of this sort and thus are in considerable part reflections of rate of evolution, which is clearly much more rapid in carnivores than in pelecypods.

Quite commonly when progressive change evolves a new type of organism, it arises from only part of the ancestral population. The old type also continues to exist, as in the now familiar example of *Ostrea* and *Gryphaea*. There are thus really three different cases. A line of descent may give off a distinctive branch but itself continue without much change; extinction has not occurred in any sense of the word. Or, second, it may change as a whole into a new type, or several; there has been an extinction of a particular type of organization but not absolute extinction of a line of descent. Third, it may cease to exist, its last representatives dying without issue; this is extinction absolute and unqualified.

It would not be quite right to say of the second of these cases that no extinction has occurred. Extinction of type is obviously different from absolute ending of a line of descent, and we could give different names to the two if we wished, but in both cases a sort of organism has disappeared from the world. Now in dealing with the record of the history of life we saw that broad types of organization tend to persist indefinitely. Extinction for them is not the rule but is decidedly exceptional. It is doubtful whether any animal phylum has ever become extinct. Of eight classes of vertebrates only one became extinct. These major grades of organization represent adaptation of a broad sort to general ways of life, such as (for Protozoa) microscopic floating life in a liquid medium (with a few other almost equally general qualifications). The possibilities for following such a general way of life have persisted, and so have the corresponding general types of organization. A more specific type of organization or, within a larger group, a single line of descent through continually interbreeding and reproducing populations, follows a way of life integrated with more particular environmental conditions. These may persist indefinitely, as they have for the "immortals" among animal types, but more commonly they tend to change over longer or shorter periods of time. Survival then demands changes in the integration of organism and environment and this, if it exceeds a certain and commonly rather narrow range of tolerance, requires evolutionary changes in the organisms. They either make these changes, in which case their former sort of organization becomes extinct, or they fail to make them and their absolute extinction ensues.

A type of organization normally persists as long as its adaptive relationships continue to be possible. Survivals of all phyla, of most classes, of a few genera, but of no species, are all exemplifications of this rule. Its obverse is exemplified by extinction of all species, of most genera, of some classes, but of no phyla.

This view of extinction needs further examination and particularization, but first it may be desirable to take brief notice of some opposing views. One of these views is that extinction is caused, sometimes or normally, by the continuation of an inherent trend which is not necessarily adaptive in nature or orientation. This possibility has already been considered in previous discussion of oriented evolution, with the conclusion that there is no strong evidence that such a thing ever did occur. It may be noted in passing that this view (and also the next to be considered) is most commonly held by those whose philosophy of evolution is vitalist, finalist, or both. I cannot help finding it very strange that anyone should think that an entelechy or vital urge should orient life toward death, or that the supernal plan followed by life has death as its goal. If—the finalist reply—these are only side lines that missed the goal, is it not impious to impute such fumbling to the Planner?

Another view is that groups of organisms become old, just as individual organisms do, that senility sets in and extinction follows from senile degeneration. Some suspicion of this forcing of the analogy has already been expressed. Examination of the supposed evidence for this phenomenon tends only to deepen the suspicion, or to convert it into a conviction, that the phenomenon does not really exist. The example most often given (first, perhaps, by the great American paleontologist Hyatt in the 1890's) involves the ammonites, a group that lends itself well to exemplification of evolutionary processes and has long been studied by a large number of the ablest investigators of these processes.

The ammonite group as a whole, consisting of marine invertebrate animals with chambered shells separated by more or less complexly plicated partitions, persisted from early Devonian, or just possibly middle Ordovician, to late Cretaceous, a span of more or less 250,000,000 years (possibly but improbably over 300,000,000). The typical or commonest form of the shell was a spiral coil in a single plane, somewhat like a heavy line coiled on a deck, except that later coils usually overlapped the earlier. In the Mesozoic some peculiar variations began to appear. (See fig. 21.) The coil might be open so that succeeding coils did not touch the earlier, or only the earliest parts might be coiled and the later perfectly straight; early coils might be followed by a straight segment and then by another coil turning back toward the early part;

the plane might be abandoned and the spiral grow upward in an asymmetrical, snaillike way, or growth might even be very irregular with no clear spiral.

Fig. 21. A few ammonites. A, the "normal" or usual, simply coiled type. B-E, some of the unusual types considered by some students as indicative of "racial old age." (Data from Boule and Piveteau.)

The claim is that these irregularities are signs of senility, that growth was no longer under proper control because of lessened vitality in racial old age. In fact such types occurred, and periodically recurred, from the Triassic onward, in other words during the whole latter half of the long history of the group. They were common during times when the group was most widespread, abundant, actively evolving, and obviously eminently "virile" and succcessful. A family particularly characterized throughout its history by such aberrant growth forms (the Lytoceratidae) was one of the longest lived of ammonite families, persisting some 90,000,000 years through the Jurassic and Cretaceous. Moreover, forms with perfectly normal plane spiral shells continued abundantly right up to the end and then became extinct along with all the others. The paleontologists who have seen evidence of senility in this history seem, beyond serious question, to have been victims of the pathetic fallacy. They have mistaken mere unusualness of shape, which was, at worst, no impediment to vigorous development and good adaptation, for the deformities of old age that beset ourselves as individuals.

It is true that the last members of a group before its extinction are frequently—not always, by any means—extreme in size, horn development, or other such features and occasionally quite bizarre. Of course if a group is changing progressively, its last members are bound to be an extreme for that group; if it had lasted longer, it would have reached new extremes. As a matter of fact, animals about as bizarre as any that ever became extinct are alive today and doing well: elephants are as queer as mammoths; living whales are far bulkier than any dinosaur; the spiral "unicorn" tooth of the narwhal has no equal for strangeness among past animals; it would be hard to imagine anything more fantastic than some insects such as the dynastes beetle or some of the mantids.

To the extent that such developments may perhaps have been involved in extinction, there are at least two concrete and established factors fully competent to account for this without calling in the vague and dubious factor of supposed racial old age. First, strong structural peculiarity usually betokens high specificity of adaptation and limits avenues of possible change, and these are certainly factors making extinction more likely. Second, when a group is already waning and approaching the danger of extinction, its local interbreeding populations eventually fall below the size where random, inadaptive mutations are regularly eliminated without becoming fixed in an undue proportion of the population. This, with accompanying excessive inbreeding also likely in such a situation, may tend to produce bizarre, sickly, or generally inadaptive forms. The process will hasten extinction, but it sets in only when extinction is already approaching. If this be defined as "racial old age," then impending extinction causes "old age," not the other way around.

The general, true cause of extinction seems to be a change in the life situation, the organism-environment integration, requiring in the organisms concerned an adaptive change which they are unable to make. The sorts of environmental changes involved may be extremely varied and the inability of the organisms to make appropriate adaptive responses is also a complex problem. A factor of prime importance is specificity of adaptation. Allusion has already been made to the wide differences shown by animals in this respect, for instance as regards diet. Obviously an animal that can live on a wide variety of different foods is more likely to survive if food in general becomes scarce or if some kinds disappear than is an animal that can eat only one kind of food.

Specificity of adaptation is what is meant in the main by specialization in evolution, and "overspecialization" is a major factor in extinction. It must, however, be noted that every animal that ever lived and all that live now are specialized to some extent: each has special life requirements and none can live in more than a small fraction of the environments offered by the earth. This universal specialization becomes overspecialization only when it fails to meet the pragmatic test of survival, and this failure can occur with any degree of specialization. If a deluge were to cover all the lands of the earth, all land animals would be overspecialized in the face of this emergency. As long as there is land to live on, land life is, for most of its practitioners, a specialization with good survival value and not an overspecialization.

There is a reciprocal relationship between breadth of specialization and likelihood of extinction. Slight environmental change will harass a group of narrow specificity in adaptation and may cause extinction if the group is not variable enough and mutable enough to make the appropriate change. Even if such a change is possible to the organisms concerned, it may be blocked if, for instance, some other group is already firmly established and well adapted in the new way of life which affords an otherwise possible escape from extinction. Larger environmental change will, as a rule, have to occur before extinction threatens a group of less specific adaptation, but in the end any group may be threatened or may become extinct if the change becomes radical enough.

Environmental change has constantly occurred and so, throughout the history of life, extinction has repeatedly befallen groups with specialization such as to be critical in the given emergency. Since the more specialized groups are more liable to extinction, it may seem remarkable that increasing specialization is nevertheless the rule in the histories of most groups of organisms and that a stage is never approached when all surviving groups have the lowest practicable specificity of adaptation. In fact, particular environmental conditions may often remain essentially constant over long periods, the critical emergency may be long delayed or may never arise. Disappearance of grass would have doomed most of the sorts of later Tertiary horses and various other animals, but grass did not disappear.

In the meantime, there is an advantage in specific adaptation as long as its environmental requisites continue. Grass is an abundant food which cannot be effectively used except by those animals specifically adapted to it. There is in evolution a continual balancing of the two advantages: the advantage of increasing specialization in sufficiently stable conditions, the advantage of versatility in changing conditions. A crude but picturesque analogy, which we will pursue no further than its validity for metaphoric description, is provided by specialization in human occupations. A highly specialized artisan such as, say, a glass-eye blower, will thrive as long as his trade is adaptive—there is a brisk demand for his products —and will be better paid than a general laborer. If there were no further demand for artificial eyes or if a cheap, improved type not blown from glass were developed, the glass-eye blower would have to change his trade or starve, while the general laborer would be unaffected.

There is also the point that one specialization may lead to

another, and here the descriptive analogy continues to hold. If glass eyes went out of demand, the blower of them might yet maintain his advantage by turning his special skills, say, to the making of glass laboratory apparatus. Specialized animals often similarly avoid extinction by, so to speak, changing their trades. Browsing horses became highly specialized and some reached a point where further and different specialization for grazing became possible. The browsers eventually all became extinct; the grazers did not. Sloths originally specialized for life on the ground and for digging. Some utilized features of this specialization convertible for a very specialized sort of arboreal life. The ground sloths are extinct; the tree sloths are not.

The particular changes that cause extinction when they affect groups unable to adapt to them are extremely varied. Any environmental change whatever may have this result. Probably one of the commonest initiators of extinction is competition. The environmental change is the development or incursion into a given region of a group of animals whose adaptations and consequent life requirements are essentially similar to those of a group already present. The two groups, different to some degree in history and origin, are necessarily not identical in structure and function. (We have already seen that parallel or convergent adaptation cannot produce complete identity.) In some respects, however slight, one group will have a balance of characteristics advantageous to it. The other group will inevitably either become extinct[8] or develop a new specialization outside the range of its successful rival.

In this process it is an interesting feature that the more specialized group usually has the advantage and is the one to retain its field of specialization. If the less specialized group does not simply become extinct, it will itself become more specialized, but specialized in a different field from that of the group with originally higher specialization. This is the process grandly exemplified in the thinning out and increasing divergence and specialization of the various lines of descent in an adaptive radiation. It helps to explain why increasing specialization is one of the most widespread features of evolution although it is also one of the commonest factors in extinction.

Extinction by competition is also the usual process in replacement of one group of organisms by another, although we

---

[8] Aside from evidence of this outcome in free nature, it has been established experimentally that extinction always occurs when two species are in competition for food and neither has means for withdrawing from the competition. See, for instance, T. Park, *Experimental Studies of Interspecies Competition. I. Competition between Populations of the Flour Beetles*, Triboleum confusum *Duval and* Triboleum castaneum *Herbst* (Ecological Monographs, *18* [1948], 265-308).

have also noted cases of delayed replacement in which the extinction has some other cause and replacement occurs after, not concurrently with, extinction.

There is another process of specialization and competition which may have had considerable importance in evolution. Competition commonly occurs not only between but also within groups of organisms. Among many polygamous mammals and birds, for instance, the males engage in overt, active competition for the females. Specialization to meet competition within the group then often involves evolution of weapons or ornaments, such as antlers in deer or trains in peacocks. Within most species there is some degree of competition, generally passive, for food or for living room, and this too may involve specialization. It is probably a factor in the frequent tendency toward larger size in evolution, for the larger animals of such groups commonly do have some advantage over the smaller in competition with their own kind. Such specialization for intragroup competition may also be of some use in intergroup competition, as would generally be true of larger size and as seems to be true to a limited extent, at least, of deer antlers. In other cases, such as that of the peacock's train, it is hard to see any possible advantage for intergroup competition and there may be a definite disadvantage. In all cases, specialization for intragroup competition, simply because it is not developed with reference to survival or successful intergroup competition by the species as a whole, is a possible disadvantage to the species in its external relationships. It may well determine the loser when intergroup competition does occur. The suggestion has also been made that it may even be carried to such a point as to cause extinction without intervention of any competitor or environmental change, but for this I can see no evidence; the sabertooth canines are sometimes given as an example here, too, and we know that they certainly did not cause extinction by their overgrowth—it is also extremely improbable that they were specializations for intragroup competition.

Particular cases of extinction, other than those evidently due to competition, are usually hard or impossible to explain in detail. It is not that there is any serious doubt about the general cause, but that possible particular causes present an embarrassment of riches and many of them can leave no clear trace in the record of earth and life history. We do not know just why horses became extinct in the Americas around the end of the Pleistocene, not because the event is inexplicable but because there is no conclusive way of choosing among possible explanations. Change of climate or topography, decreasing food supply, spread of poisonous plants, incursion of new beasts of prey (such as man, in this case), outbreak of epidemic disease, and many other possibilities come into consideration in such cases. Some can sometimes be shown to be improbable, but elimination can seldom be carried down to one possibility, and indeed in many cases it is probably an accumulation of changes and not one alone that initiates extinction. The process is also cumulative, because once a group has begun to decline it will sooner or later reach a critical point beyond which the final elimination may be produced by factors that would have had no fatal influence while the group was abundant. Among factors of this sort are seasonal fluctuations in numbers, unchecked inadaptive mutation, excessive inbreeding (with resulting undue proportions of disadvantageous or lethal homozygous recessives), or geographic restriction—so that purely local conditions or catastrophes may affect the fate of the whole group, as they cannot in a group that is widespread.

It is not intended to stress environmental changes as if they were in themselves the cause of extinction. No such change can cause extinction if the organisms affected also change in an appropriate way. On the other hand, we have seen that organisms can survive indefinitely without changing in any essential. It is neither the change in environment nor the lack of change in the organisms that causes extinction: it is the two together. Much of the long scientific discussion of theories of evolution has turned on the question whether evolution is fundamentally autogenetic (or autonomic) or ectogenetic, that is, whether the driving factors in the history of life have been internal to the organisms or external to them (environmental). It is becoming more and more clear that this a false issue. The truth is not in one or the other of these alternatives but in a third which combines the two and yet has essential features of its own.

6. *Forces of Evolution and Their Integration*

THE COURSE of evolution is marked by changes in structures and functions as these appear in individual organisms. The evolutionary forces act, of necessity, on individuals, but their effects are not achieved within single individuals. These effects work out within associated groups of individuals, populations, and over the course of successive generations. A key to the process is, then, that evolutionary changes must arise in or must, at least, be transmitted by whatever it is that passes from one generation to the next, by the heredity of the group. The association of individuals into populations that is important in this process must therefore be reproductive association. The group that actually evolves is a group linked together by exchange and transmission of hereditary factors, a population of individuals that interbreed over the course of generations. It is true that the survival of individuals in a community and their success in producing new generations may be strongly affected by nonbreeding members of the community (such as the unsexed workers in insect societies and the older or otherwise nonbreeding members of human society). In the special circumstances of communal life the nonbreeders too may thus have an important role in evolution. It is nevertheless fundamental that evolutionary change consists basically of change in heredity and that this is developed in interbreeding populations.

Most of heredity is carried by genes, self-reproducing chemical units within the cells of organisms, which are aggregated into groups, chromosomes, that also usually reproduce or reduplicate themselves faithfully whenever one cell divides into two. These chromosomes, with their included genes, are passed on from one generation to the next, usually within specialized germ cells from which individuals of the new generation develop. Their development is controlled or determined in greatest part by the genes and chromosomes received from parents, and under this control it follows a pattern which produces characteristic body forms and physiological systems similar to those of the parents.

Heredity is, on the whole, a conservative factor tending to keep succeeding generations within a common pattern. The acorn produces an oak similar to the tree that produced the acorn, except in unessential details, and the egg produces a chicken essentially like the hen that laid it. We know, nevertheless, that offspring are never *precisely* like their parents, and since evolution is a process of change these differences are of special concern to us here. Such differences may arise in three ways, and in these ways only.

In the first place, the development of the individual is affected not only by the inherited growth determinants but also by the conditions under which growth occurs. Like most of the processes important in evolution, individual development turns out on closer examination to be neither purely autogenous nor purely ectogenous but a combination of the two. No two oak trees, even if grown from twin acorns, have exactly the same size, shape, placing of limbs, number of leaves, etc. Greater or less differences in the environment (for instance in soil or local weather) affect them as they grow, no matter how near each other they may be. Such effects occur to markedly different degrees in different sorts of organisms. When seeds or eggs are simply cast adrift to develop as best they may, their development is strongly affected by the environment. Plants as a whole have much more of such environmentally induced variation than do animals. At the other extreme, probably the most important feature of the mammals is that in them this sort of variation is reduced to a minimum. Development within the nearly uniform environment of the womb followed by maternal care and milk feeding ensures reproduction about as true to type as may be, although of course even here absolute uniformity of the conditions surrounding growth is not obtainable. Grosser changes are still caused by disease and accident, and different activities of the organisms themselves cause change in them, as, for instance, exercise may increase the size of a muscle or lack of use decrease it.

Differences between parents and offspring arising in this way are not hereditary. It was long supposed that they were and a whole theory of evolution, to be mentioned later for its historical interest, was based on this belief; but this has now been disproved beyond reasonable doubt. It is, nevertheless, going too far to suppose that such changes have nothing to do with evolution. They are not themselves changes in heredity such as, in a fundamental sense, constitute evolution, but they may have a decided influence on these hereditary changes. Adaptation to local environment during growth may have definite survival value to the individual and affect its passing on of heredity to future generations. Any individual change not itself hereditary may nevertheless strongly influence the individual's ability or opportunity to reproduce, and in this indirect way will affect the course of evolution of the group as a whole. Individual flexibility is also itself an essential characteristic that is heritable and that evolves.

A second, and, from an evolutionary point of view, far more important source of differences between parents and offspring is in the mechanism of sexual reproduction, which is not quite, but nearly, universal among both plants and animals. (Even the protozoans, which usually reproduce by simple fission of the whole body, normally undergo from time to time a form of sexual reproduction.) The offspring receive chromosomes, and hence genes that are bundled into chromosomes, from two different sources, usually an equal number from each in corresponding pairs. It is extremely unusual for two individuals to have identical sets of genes, so that the chromosomes received from the two parents in sexual reproduction are practically always different in some respects. The combination of the two sets in the offspring thus differs from that in either parent. There is also involved in this process occasional transfer of genes between the two chromosomes in a pair. When the offspring, in turn, come to reproduce, each passes on to its progeny not simply the set of chromosomes it received from one parent or the other, but a random selection from both sets.

Thus in continued sexual reproduction through the generations the genes and chromosomes are constantly being reshuffled. Even in organisms with relatively simple gene sets and few chromosomes, the number of possible combinations of different genes and dissimilar chromosomes is astronomically large, far larger than the number of individual organisms in the line of successive interbreeding populations. It is rare for any two individuals to have exactly the same sets of these heredity determinants; practically speaking this can happen only when they are identical twins, developed from a single fertilized egg—and such twins, although exactly like each other in heredity, will almost never be exactly like either of their parents. Heredity is essentially conservative in its broad outlines, but this mechanism of shuffling in sexual reproduction makes it almost endlessly varied in detail.

Such changes between parents and offspring are hereditary, subject to continuation of the same sort of shuffling that produces them, and are therefore materials available for basic evolutionary change. Combinations produced in the shuffling process are not necessarily soon lost again by reshuffling. Recombination of genes within single chromosomes is an occasional, not an invariable, process and it is not wholly random. Particular combinations of chromosome pairs, even though produced at random, become more frequent in the population if each sort of chromosome involved becomes more frequent. Identity of all the thousands of genes and of the several or dozens of pairs of chromosomes is exceedingly rare between any two individuals, but similar groupings and identity of certain limited combinations of a few key genes may readily be developed within a large proportion or all of a population.

The role of these changes in evolution is important, but it has limits. New combinations of genes and chromosomes produce new variant sorts of organisms, but no basically new types of organisms can arise and evolutionary change cannot be long sustained, geologically speaking, as long as the genes and chromosome sets remain of the same kinds. Major and long-continued evolutionary changes therefore depend on a third source of difference between parents and offspring: mutations, which are the production of new sorts of genes and chromosome sets. Chromosome mutations may change the number of chromosomes (a change fairly common in plants but much less so in animals) or their form and character, for instance by reduplication of segments, or reversal in their position within the chromosome, or their transfer from one chromosome to another. Such differences may or may not have more far-reaching effects than reshuffling of existing genes and chromosome sets, but they too are limited by the fact that the same sorts of genes, the ultimate determinants as far as we know, continue to appear in them. The most basic changes involved in evolution are gene mutations, the rise of new sorts of genes.

Precisely what happens when a gene mutates is not yet known. For that matter, it is not yet known precisely what a gene is, except that it must be a unit in the chemical make-up of a chromosome and that a mutation must be a change in the structure or composition of that unit. Among the facts of particular evolutionary importance that are known about genes are these: they are inherited as discrete, unblending units but they act in development as interacting and coopera-tive sets; they do not correspond in a one-to-one relationship with structures of the developed organism but affect or con-trol the growth pattern from which those structures arise; through this growth control single genes may have effects on various different structures and characters (this is called pleiotropism); one gene or several may modify the action of another; and a single character may depend for its develop-ment on the presence and interaction of a number of different genes.

Some of the things known about gene mutation and im-portant for study of evolution are these:

Some genes are very stable, some mutate with considerable frequency; it is probable that all can and do mutate in time. Frequency of mutation may be changed by various influ-ences such as the presence of certain other genes or applica-tion of heat, radiation, or chemicals; but with some qualifica-tions the nature of the mutation is not determined by such influences. The effect of a single mutation on structural or physiological characters may be almost imperceptible or may result in obvious and radical changes in the whole body. "Large" mutations, those with the greatest effects on the or-ganism, are commonly, but not necessarily, lethal, preventing development of the fertilized egg or bringing early death to the developing individual. Most important of all, from our present point of view, the effects of gene mutations have no evident relationship to the adaptive status, needs, or general

way of life of the organism involved. They are in this respect entirely random. This is true, too, of induced mutations;
for instance, the effects of those caused by application of heat
have no particular relationship to adaptation to temperature
of environment. In an organism already well adapted, almost
all mutations will be disadvantageous in the previously fixed
way of life, simply because in such conditions any random
change is likely to be for the worse. The change may, however, or may not, be advantageous in some other way of life
which may, or again may not, be accessible to the organism.[1]

One of the frontiers of modern genetical and evolutionary
research is study of the way in which mutations affect different stages in development of the organism and the evolutionary roles of such effects. The different possibilities have been
explored in considerable detail and a technical name has been
given to each. Some of these names have a certain awesome
fascination ("lipopalingenesis," for example) but they need
not delay us here. Changes made evident only in later stages
of development generally have rather slight effects on final
outcome. If they consist essentially of additions at the end of
the developmental process, they leave most of that process,
as inherited from the ancestry, intact. This sort of change, which
is common but far from universal and seldom entirely clear-
cut in the evolutionary process, is responsible for the usual
very rough approximation of successive ancestral stages in
the development of the individual in accordance with the
overgeneralized and much abused aphorism of the nineteenth-century evolutionists that "ontogeny repeats phylogeny."

On the other hand, the effects of a mutation may start to
operate early in the development of the individual. There is
some ground for suspicion, although the point is disputed
and cannot be said to be established, that this is the usual
course, that mutations ordinarily affect the whole process
of development. Their effects may, of course, be more evident in one stage or another. If those effects are slight but
cumulative, they may not be noticeable until late stages and
may be supposed to be confined to those stages. In any event,

[1] The serious enquirer should supplement this minimal presentation of such facts
of genetics as are absolutely necessary for understanding of the meaning of evolution
by reading some modern treatment of genetics as a whole, such as E. W. Sinnott,
L. C. Dunn, and Th. Dobzhansky, *Principles of Genetics* (New York and London, McGraw-Hill, 1950). Th. Dobzhansky's *Genetics and the Origin of Species*
(2d ed. New York, Columbia University Press, 1941), which takes for granted
knowledge of the elements of genetics, is extremely important. It has had a fundamental influence on current comprehension of evolution, and my own understanding
and discussion of the subject, throughout this book and otherwise, have drawn
heavily on it. Basic principles of heredity and their bearing on the human situation are also summarized in a more popular way in L. C. Dunn, and Th. Dobzhansky, *Heredity, Race and Society* (New York, The New American Library of World
Literature, Inc., 1946).

if effects are really confined to late stages, their results cannot be very profound, but if they begin to appear early in development the final results may show radical changes from the parental condition, or may again be only slight. A marked alteration of early course of development with consequent still more marked changes in final structure seems to be the usual mechanism for "large" mutations. This in turn provides a possible mechanism for sudden origin of new structural types in evolution. The possibility is evident, but its general significance in evolution is strongly disputed, and especially the question whether this is the way in which basic new types usually arise. This dispute will be mentioned again.

The random nature of changes in heredity must be particularly emphasized. The shuffling of existing stocks of genes in sexual reproduction is, in the main, random. The appearance of chromosome and gene mutations is also largely, although not completely, random and the nature of their effects seems to be altogether random with respect to the needs or adaptation of the organisms and with respect to the direction in which evolution has, in fact, been progressing in the given group. This led some of the earlier students of heredity to think that evolution is really a wholly random process. "Early" here means only a generation or so ago, for almost all of our real knowledge of how heredity works has been gained in the last fifty years.

In examination of the phenomena of evolution, we have seen that there are indeed elements in these that appear to be erratic and to arise at random. The source of these random effects has now been identified: it is, narrowly, mutation or, more broadly, the largely random operation of the whole mechanism of heredity. We also saw, however, that many of the phenomena of evolution are clearly oriented to some degree. The history of life has not been strictly random or strictly oriented, but an odd mixture of the two, with one predominant here and the other there, but both generally present and almost inextricably combined in the evolution of any particular group. The orienting element was found rather surely to be adaptation, and not such proposed alternatives as innate life tendency or progression toward a destined goal according to plan. Since it has been found that the materials for change are largely random, the question naturally arises as to how evolutionary change can be so extensively nonrandom, how adaptation can orient it.

The mechanism of adaptation is natural selection. The idea of natural selection is very simple, even though its operation is highly complex and may be extremely subtle. Natural selection has this basis: in every population some individuals have more offspring than others. This obvious fact automatically accounts for the possibility of evolutionary change. It has been seen that individuals in any group differ in genetic make-up, hence pass on different heredity to their offspring, and also that mutations occur in a scattered way as such a group reproduces. It may happen, and is indeed the usual thing over small numbers of generations, that the new generation, in spite of its differences between individuals, has about the same average genetic constitution as the parent generation and about the same incidence of mutations, so that no clearly evident change occurs from one generation to the next. It is, however, extremely unlikely that the new generation will have exactly the same genetic make-up as the parental generation. Some individuals do have more offspring than others and their particular genetic characters, which differ to some degree from those of other individuals, will be more frequent in the new generation. The difference may be imperceptibly slight or it may be quite marked, even in production of a single generation.

Even a very slight change will produce evident, eventually large effects if it is cumulative from one generation to the next. This results if there is some constant factor such that, on an average, the individuals that do have more offspring in each generation are those tending toward the same hereditary type; in other words, if they are somehow selected for characteristics that have a hereditary basis. In nature the individuals that tend to have more offspring are, as a rule and no matter how slight the difference, either those best integrated with their environment (including the association with their own species) and most successful in it or those best able to begin to exploit an opportunity not available or less so to their neighbors. Thus natural selection usually operates in favor either of increased adaptation to a given way of life, organism-environment integration, or of such change as will bring about adaptation to another, accessible way of life. Natural selection thus orients evolutionary change in the direction of one or another of these two sorts of adaptation. We have seen, in fact, that these are the directions of orientation in evolution, to the extent that such orientation is effective.

Natural selection as it was understood in Darwinian days emphasized "the struggle for existence" and "the survival of the fittest." These concepts had ethical, ideological, and political repercussions which were and continue to be, in some cases, unfortunate, to say the least. Even modern students of evolution have not always fully corrected the misconceptions arising from these slogans. It should now be clear that the process does not depend on "existence" or "survival," certainly not as this applies to individuals and not even in any intensive or explanatory way as it applies to populations or species. It depends on differential reproduction, which is a different matter altogether. It does not favor "the fittest," flatly and just so, unless you care to circle around and define "fittest" as those that do have most offspring. It does favor those that have more offspring. This usually means those best adapted to the conditions in which they find themselves or those best able to meet opportunity or necessity for adaptation to other existing conditions, which may or may not mean that they are "fittest," according to understanding of that word. Moreover the correlation between those having more offspring, and therefore really favored by natural selection, and those best adapted or best adapting to change is neither perfect nor invariable; it is only approximate and usual.

It is, however, the word "struggle" that has led to most serious misunderstanding of the process of natural selection, along with a host of related phrases and ideas, "nature red in fang and claw," "class struggle" as a natural and desirable element in societal evolution, and all the rest. "Struggle" inevitably carries the connotation of direct and conscious combat. Such combat does occur in nature, to be sure, and it may have some connection with differential reproduction. A puma and a deer may struggle, one to kill and the other to avoid being killed. If the puma wins, it eats and presumably may thereby be helped to produce offspring, while the deer dies and will never reproduce again. Two stags may struggle in rivalry for does and the successful combatant may then reproduce while the loser does not. Even such actual struggles may have only slight effects on reproduction, although they will, on an average, tend to exercise some selective influence. The deer most likely to be killed by the puma is too old to reproduce; if the puma does not get the deer, it will eat something else; the losing stag finds other females, or a third enjoys the does while the combat rages between these two.

To generalize from such incidents that natural selection is over-all and even in a figurative sense the outcome of struggle is quite unjustified under the modern understanding of the process. Struggle is sometimes involved, but it usually is not, and when it is, it may even work against rather than toward natural selection. Advantage in differential reproduction is usually a peaceful process in which the concept of struggle is really irrelevant. It more often involves such things as better integration into the ecological situation, maintenance of a balance of nature, more efficient utilization of available food, better care of the young, elimination of intragroup discords (struggles) that might hamper reproduction, exploitation of environmental possibilities that are not the objects of competition[2] or are less effectively exploited by others.

It is to be emphasized that the group of its own kind among which an animal lives is also a part of its environment, but a special part. There is an intraspecific selection, based on integration and association within the group, as well as extraspecific selection, based on adaptive relationship to the environment as a whole. (The same sort of distinction was made in discussing specialization and competition in relationship to extinction.) Intragroup selection may involve actual struggle, as in the case of the stags fighting for a doe. It may then be deleterious as regards extragroup adaptation and involve selection opposed to extragroup selection. If such is the case, the result, as Haldane has emphasized, may be deleterious for the species as a whole, although even here we may remark that intra- and extragroup struggle commonly produce selection in the same direction. It is to be added that in intragroup selection, also, struggle is not necessarily or even usually of the essence. Precisely the opposite, selection in favor of harmonious or cooperative group association, is certainly common.

It was a crude concept of natural selection to think of it simply as something imposed on the species from the outside. It is not, as in the metaphor often used with reference to Darwinian selection, a sieve through which organisms are sifted, some variations passing (surviving) and some being held back (dying). It is rather a process intricately woven into the whole life of the group, equally present in the life and death of the individuals, in the associative relationships of the population, and in their extraspecific adaptations.

A criticism often leveled against Darwinian natural selection, but no longer valid against the modern conception of this process, was that it seemed to be a purely negative factor in evolution and one that could not account for positive aspects in the orientation of evolution. Some role for selection was admitted, as it must be, but it was maintained that this role was merely the elimination of some individuals or types of organisms: the "unfit." Such negative action seemed

[2] The word "competition," used in discussion here and previously, may also carry anthropomorphic undertones and then be subject to some of these same objections. It may, however, and in this connection it must, be understood without necessary implication of active competitive behavior. Competition in evolution often or usually is entirely passive; it could conceivably occur without the competing forms ever coming into sight or contact.

to have no particular bearing on the origin of new types or on the maintenance of positive adaptive change in evolutionary trends. This negative aspect obviously exists, but it is now evident that selection also has a positive and creative role and that it is indeed the decisive, the orienting, process in continuing adaptation. Part of the difficulty lay again in thinking in terms of struggle and survival, the death of one animal and the triumph of its enemy or rival. The concept of evolution as change in proportions, combinations, and nature of genetic factors in populations is of more recent development and this entails consequences not yet, it would seem, fully understood by the remaining critics of natural selection as the guiding force in evolution.

Selection is not primarily a process of elimination. It is a process of differential reproduction and this involves complex and delicate interplay with those genetic factors in populations that are the substantial basis of evolutionary continuity and change. In terms of single, arising mutations, those that are unfavorable will be eliminated by selection, as far as its force is effective. (The theory does not demand and the facts do not indicate that selection is always effective, or that at its most effective it can eliminate all unfavorable mutations immediately.) Those that are favorable will, however, tend under the influence of selection to spread through the population increasingly in successive generations. This, in itself, is a positive evolutionary change which is due to natural selection.

Further, the characteristics of an organism as an integrated whole depend not on the action of one gene or another but on the whole interacting set of genes. Some combinations produce poorly integrated organisms, others well-integrated ones. There are, moreover, myriads of different possible combinations even within one population that are all capable of producing workable integration but that produce each a different variant in type. As has been mentioned, the possible number of such combinations vastly exceeds the whole number of individual organisms that can ever exist within a given population or species. Only a fraction of the possible combinations is actually realized in a concrete, existing organism. The chances of such realization for any particular combinations depend on the frequencies in the parental population of the genes involved in the combination. These frequencies, in turn, are to considerable extent if not absolutely determined by the action of natural selection. Selection thus plays an essential part in determining what combinations of genes will be incorporated in individual organisms and so in the actual origin of new variant sorts of organisms. In this role, selection may surely be said to be a creative factor in evolution. Still further, once such favorable or adaptive combinations have arisen, selection tends to hold them together, to keep them from being shuffled apart again in the random processes of heredity in reproduction, and tends to promote their spread through the population.[3]

The way in which selection and the other factors and forces of evolution interact within a population has been worked out in a brilliant series of studies by R. A. Fisher, J. B. S. Haldane, Sewall Wright, and others.[4] It is these studies, more than anything else, that have made possible the synthesis of generations of observations and experiments in a wide variety of fields into a coherent and comprehensive modern theory of evolution. For the reader who may have browsed widely in the literature of evolution and who may have become bewildered by continuing divergences of opinion, here is a touchstone: I think it fair to say that no discussion of evolutionary theory need now be taken seriously if it does not reflect knowledge of these studies and does not take them strongly into account.

The evolutionary materials involved in this complex process are the genetical systems existing in the population and the mutations arising in these. The interacting forces producing evolutionary change from these materials are their shuffling in the process of reproduction, the incidence of mutations (their nature and rate), and natural selection.

The genetical systems existing in a population determine (in further interaction with the environment in each individual case) the nature of the organisms comprising that population. The variety of these systems—and they always are more or less varied—determines the variability of the population. This has extreme importance for evolution, because it is directly on or through this variability that natural selection operates. Limited variability offers correspondingly limited chance of rapid change or of local adaptation to particular conditions, but on the other hand in a population that is well adapted it holds a larger proportion of the population at an optimum, the best adaptive type under existing conditions. Wide variability offers the possibility of rapid (but not in-

[3] This creative aspect of selection has been discussed somewhat more fully in G. G. Simpson "The Problem of Plan and Purpose in Nature" (*Sci. Monthly, 64* [1947], 481–495).

[4] R. A. Fisher, *The Genetical Theory of Natural Selection* (Oxford, Clarendon Press, 1930); J. B. S. Haldane, *The Causes of Evolution* (New York and London, Harper, 1932); S. Wright, "Statistical Genetics and Evolution" (*Bull. Amer. Math. Soc., 48* [1942], 233–246. These authors and others have written numerous other studies of aspects of this subject. The cited paper by Wright is only one in a long sequence of short contributions made over a period of about twenty years which unfortunately have not been gathered into a comprehensive publication by their author.

definitely continued) evolutionary change, quick adjustment to environmental changes, and local adaptation to special conditions within the wider range of the whole population. But it means that some proportion, perhaps a considerable proportion, of the population will deviate markedly from the optimum condition, will not be as well adapted as they might be. As in so many evolutionary phenomena there is here a complex interplay, a balancing of opposed advantages and of other factors.

Another important fact to be mentioned only in passing in this necessarily brief review of a very complicated subject is the existence in populations of hidden variability, which can be evoked under the influence of selection or in other ways. This involves the usual presence in populations of genes (especially the recessives of the geneticists) whose action is prevented or overlain in the presence of other genes (especially the dominant alleles of the geneticists) which may be more common in the population. If the general proportion of genes with hidden effects rises in the population, they will more often occur in pairs in the same individual (which is then recessive homozygous in genetical terms) rather than in combination with their concealing equivalent genes (in heterozygous combination), and their effect will then appear.

In a population indefinitely large, breeding wholly at random, not affected by selection, the proportions of the various existing sorts of genes and chromosomes will tend toward definite fixed ratios. When this equilibrium is reached, change in genetic ratios and consequently evolutionary change will cease. The population will still vary, but the variability will be constant in nature and extent. This condition does not occur and evolutionary change does ensue because populations are of limited size, because they do not breed entirely at random, because new sorts of genes and chromosomes arise by mutation, and because selection does act on the population.

The outcome of the shuffling process and the effectiveness, absolute and relative, of mutation and selection are largely dependent on the size and breeding pattern of the population. Almost any variation in genetic system and almost any mutation will be affected to some extent by selection, even though the effect may be exceedingly slight. It is rare for such random variations and mutations to have no selective advantage or disadvantage whatsoever. Whatever the influence of selection may be, there is always some chance that these random changes will become established in a certain proportion of the population or even that they will spread to the whole population in succeeding generations. This is one reason why evolution is not completely adaptive and does show random influences. Other reasons are that selection can act only on variations that do occur, which arise at random and are not necessarily or usually the best possible from the point of view of adaptation, and that a given mutation, for instance, commonly has multiple effects some of which are adaptive and others nonadaptive or inadaptive.

Selection almost always has some effect on the fixation or elimination of favorable or unfavorable random changes. The chances of fixation in a population of given size and structure are proportional to intensity of selection for or against, although the chances are very rarely quite 100 per cent or 0. For a given intensity of selection, these chances tend to vary with size of the breeding population. The exact relationships are, again, rather complicated, but the general tendency is for selection to be more effective the larger the population. In large interbreeding populations the chances of spread of a variation purely at random become very slight: favorable selection, even if very slight in degree, will usually ensure such spread and unfavorable selection will usually prevent it. Evolution in large populations is dominated by selection, tends to be closely proportional to the intensity of selection, and tends to have only few and extremely slow changes that are not purely and directly adaptive. It is just such groups that do show, in their evolutionary records, clear and long-continued trends adaptive in control. It is also such groups, with large and widespread populations, that tend to leave more abundant and more continuous fossil records, which doubtless helps to account for the impression on some paleontologists that evolution usually or always follows well-defined trends.

On the other hand, in small breeding populations the effectiveness of selection may be greatly reduced. The chances of merely random change are correspondingly increased. In very small populations, of only a few dozens or perhaps at most hundreds of individuals, evolutionary change may be mainly at random and the influence of selection may be almost negligible unless the intensity of selection is unusually great. Such random evolution is almost always inadaptive and its usual outcome is extinction.

Continuous and evenly distributed interbreeding within a whole population (say the whole of a given species) is not the rule in nature or in human society and, indeed, is perhaps never fully exemplified. In the usual situation, there are local groups that habitually interbreed, with greater or less inbreeding of their various family strains. (In man, these groups are defined not only by geographic proximity but also by social and occupational status, intellectual level, and other societal factors such as religion.) Between such groups there is a certain but limited amount of crossbreeding, with consequent flow of genetic factors between groups through the generations. The ideal situation for maintenance of continuously good adaptation, including rapid evolution when adaptive change is possible or necessary, seems to involve a relatively large total population divided into a large number of moderate sized local breeding groups, with some continual gene interchange (crossbreeding) between adjacent groups.

With this understanding of the evolutionary process as it really works in populations of organisms and on the factors that determine their heredity, adaptation ceases to be a miracle, or even a serious problem. It is adaptation that gives an appearance of purposefulness in evolution and in its results in the present world of life. Its explanation was the main stumbling block in acceptance of evolution as a fact, and later in attempts to explain the course of evolution by one theory or another. Failures of earlier materialistic attempts to explain this apparent purposefulness were responsible, in large part, for the conclusions of some students that this betokened purpose, in fact, and of certain among these that the purpose betokened a Purposer. It would be brash, indeed, to claim complete understanding of this extraordinarily intricate process, but it does seem that the problem is now essentially solved and that the mechanism of adaptation is known. It turns out to be basically materialistic, with no sign of purpose as a working variable in life history, and with any possible Purposer pushed back to the incomprehensible position of First Cause.

A constant stumbling block in the way of attempts to understand evolution has been that its processes must explain not only adaptation but also absence of adaptation, the existence and persistence of random as well as of oriented features in evolution. This was, and remains, an unanswered argument against theories demanding the reality of purpose or the existence of a goal in evolution. It equally renders untenable all the other theories that attempted to explain evolution by the dominant or exclusive action of one single principle or another, such as the neo-Darwinian insistence on natural selection as essentially the whole story. Modern understanding of evolution is not as simple as were these various theories, but their simplicity was factitious. They were bound to be wrong in seeking a simple explanation for something that is, in its nature and its phenomena, so far from simple.

The presence, often simultaneously, of both adaptive and nonadaptive, both apparently purposeful and apparently purposeless, both oriented and random features in evolution has now been sufficiently explained. Nonadaptive and random changes have another possible role in evolution which is important and which has so far been suggested only in passing. They have a bearing on changes in broad types of organization, the appearance of new phyla, classes, or other major groups in the course of the history of life. The process by which such radical events occur in evolution is the subject of one of the most serious remaining disputes among qualified professional students of evolution. The question is whether such major events take place instantaneously, by some process essentially unlike those involved in lesser or more gradual evolutionary change, or whether all of evolution, including these major changes, is explained by the same principles and processes throughout, their results being greater or less according to the time involved, the relative intensity of selection, and other material variables in any given situation.[5]

Possibility for such dispute exists because transitions between major grades of organization are seldom well recorded by fossils. There is in this respect a tendency toward systematic deficiency in the record of the history of life. It is thus possible to claim that such transitions are not recorded because they did not exist, that the changes were not by transition but by sudden leaps in evolution. There is much diversity of opinion as to just how such leaps are supposed to happen. Beurlen, for instance, ascribes them vaguely and vitalistically to an inner urge or will on the part of the organisms concerned. Goldschmidt ascribes them to a sudden over-all remodeling of the genetic system, "systemic mutation" different in kind from the well-known gene and chromosome mutations of more orthodox genetics. Schindewolf thinks that they are mutations, apparently of the usual sort, but large mutations that markedly change the course of individual development from its early stages and thus produce radically new adult forms.

It is impossible in a brief space, and it is unnecessary for present purposes, to discuss the pros and cons of this argument in detail. Enough has, indeed, already been said to throw some of the more extreme views out of court without further hearing. "A will toward individualization and independence" is a resplendent phrase but one essentially mean-

---

[5] The former opinion is adopted by Schindewolf in his work previously cited, and is also strongly supported by K. Beurlen, *Die stammesgeschichtlichen Grundlagen der Abstammungslehre* (Jena, Gustav Fischer, 1937); and R. Goldschmidt, *The Material Basis of Evolution* (New Haven, Yale University Press, 1940). The subject is particularly well reviewed and the arguments of Schindewolf, Beurlen, Goldschmidt, and others of their school strongly and I think conclusively refuted in Rensch, *op. cit.*

ingless in the face of actual evolutionary processes as these are now known. "Systemic mutations," which have never been observed and the supposed nature of which has not been concretely described, need not be taken seriously if, as is the case, the phenomena that they were postulated to explain can be explained in terms of known processes and forces.[6] If only ordinary, but "large," mutations are supposed to be involved, then we are back within the framework of the modern materialistic theory, although of course we would still like to know, and will still be constrained to discuss, the relative parts played in evolution by large and small mutations.

Transitional types are not invariably lacking in the record. A multitude of them are known between species, many between genera, a few between classes, but none, it is true, between phyla. Most of the phyla appear toward the beginning of the Paleozoic, as discussed in Chapter I, and the absence of record of prior ancestral types is as hard or as easy to explain whether we suppose that they arose instantaneously or gradually. The record is obviously a sampling only and full of gaps. We would suppose that if all changes were by slow transition we still would find only a small proportion of the transitional types and might find none between the phyla, few in number and with their special conditions of early preservation. On the other hand, if major changes were always instantaneous, obviously we should find no transitional types—and we do find many of them. If we did not happen to have found such types between fishes and amphibians, amphibians and reptiles, reptiles and birds on one hand and mammals on the other, or even between eohippus and the horse, these particular changes would surely be considered instantaneous by students who incline to that view. As H. E. Wood has remarked, the argument from absence of transitional types boils down to the striking fact that such types are always lacking unless they have been found.

As far as analysis has been carried on living forms, distinct populations, with their separate characteristics, do not customarily differ in presence or absence of single mutations but in having different, integrated genetic systems, which may involve differences in dozens, hundreds, or thousands of individual genes. On this point Goldschmidt's analysis seems sound and extremely suggestive, although his conclusion

[6] In some of his latest work Goldschmidt has implicitly retreated from his position by suggesting that his theory differs from that of almost all his genetical colleagues as regards only the size of the mutations involved, not their nature. If this emendation be accepted, the difference of opinion, as with Schindewolf's views in contrast with those of most other paleontologists, no longer has any fundamental importance for evolutionary theory, although most of the many and strong objections to his views still stand.

that therefore the difference arises by "systemic mutation" is a non sequitur. A mutation produces discrete differences and to this extent its appearance is an instantaneous and discontinuous evolutionary event, whether its effects be small or large. But it is populations, not individuals, that evolve. For a given mutation, regardless of its "size," to become involved in the origin of a new and especially of a highly distinctive group of animals it must spread through a population and while doing so and thereafter it must become integrated in a new sort of genetic system.[7] It is very nearly impossible to imagine these processes occurring except by transition over a long sequence of generations, and certainly no conclusive, or even really suggestive, opposite example is provided by the paleontological record.

It is evident that these processes, which are normal in evolution, could possibly occur with large mutations as well as small. They are, however, far more likely to occur with small mutations than with large. The chance that a mutation will be favored by selection and the chance that it will or can be integrated into a genetic system as a whole are inversely related to the effect of the mutation on the organism. If this effect is really radical, comparable, say, to the difference between one family and another (a fortiori, to that between higher categories) in the recent fauna, the chances that the mutation will really take, so to speak, and lead to an evolutionary progression are so small as to be almost negligible. On the other hand, the cumulative effect of mutations so small as to have almost imperceptible effects, each spread in the population and each successively integrated into the genetic system under the influence of selection, is more than adequate to account for transitions from one structural grade to another in the time that the record shows was expended, or was available, in such cases.

It is thus likely, to say the least, that major as well as minor changes in evolution have occurred gradually and that the same forces are at work in each case. Nevertheless there is a difference and many of the major changes cannot be considered as simply caused by longer continuation of the more usual sorts of minor changes. For one thing there is excellent evidence that evolution involving major changes often occurs with unusual rapidity, although, as we have seen, there is no good evidence that it ever occurs instantaneously. The rate of evolution of the insectivore forelimb into the bat wing,

---

[7] This special aspect of evolution is expertly treated in C. D. Darlington, *The Evolution of Genetic Systems* (Cambridge, England, Cambridge University Press, 1939). See also C. H. Waddington, *An Introduction to Modern Genetics* (New York, Macmillan, 1939); and his "Evolution of Developmental Systems" (*Nature*, 147 [1941], 108-110).

to give just one striking example, must have been many times more rapid than any evolution of the bat wing after it had arisen. The whole record attests that the origin of a distinctly new adaptive type normally occurs at a much higher rate than subsequent progressive adaptation and diversification within that type. The rapidity of such shifts from one adaptive level or equilibrium to another has suggested the name "quantum evolution," under which I have elsewhere discussed this phenomenon at greater length.[8]

Another peculiarity of such evolutionary events is that they always represent distinct changes in the direction of evolution. Such changes may occur even though the trend is continuously adaptive and its control is by natural selection throughout. Change from browsing to grazing in horses is a clear and fully documented example. The same is probably true of changes more radical in character and usually less well documented. The now fairly well known fish-amphibian transition, for instance, has no probably nonadaptive features as regards the essential changes involved. Yet we sense in many such changes that here the random element in evolution has been involved. The change-over from reptile to mammal, for instance, involved a long and adaptive trend in the reptiles, but at the last, in the switch from one type of ear to the other, for instance, there seems to be a sort of non sequitur or random experimentalism. The broadly opportunistic pattern of nature also suggests something of the same thing.

In such cases and in other instances of rather rapid change, great or small, in adaptive type, it is possible, at least, that random preadaptation has occurred. The possibility of this process has long been recognized and many geneticists formerly assigned to it a wide, even an all-embracing importance in evolution, which was almost certainly much overemphasized. By "preadaptation" is meant the random origin, by mutation, of characteristics nonadaptive or inadaptive for the ancestral way of life, but adaptive for some other way of life which happens to be available.[9] As a rule the spread, integration, and concomitant utilization of such a change could occur only under the influence of selection, and then this is only a special case of adaptation—adaptation changing its direction—and to call it preadaptation may merely be juggling with words and not establishing a real distinction. It is, however, possible for mutations occasionally to become

[8] In *Tempo and Mode in Evolution*, previously cited. The term "quantum" in this connection has been subjected to some criticism and indeed it is not very satisfactory, but no one has yet suggested a better.

[9] Interesting discussion and exemplification of this phenomenon, written when it was being given undue importance, will be found in L. Cuénot, *L'Adaptation* (Paris, G. Doin, 1925).

established without benefit of selection, or even in the face of adverse selection, especially in very small populations. Almost always this would lead to extinction, for the group could not survive long if definitely and continuously disadvantageous characters became established. In the odd case permitted by the qualification "almost," however, the characters disadvantageous in a current way of life might become advantageous where a change in way of life was possible and occurred. This true preadaptation, although probably extremely rare in evolution, provides a mechanism for sudden and erratic changes in adaptive type. The importance of such an event could be great, even though its occurrence were markedly exceptional. Rise of radically new types of organisms is certainly exceptional.

At the other end of the scale of evolutionary phenomena are the features of deployment of populations, of their adaptations to merely local variations in conditions, and of their splitting into two or more discrete populations when interbreeding ceases between subdivisions of them. Under the name of "speciation," these processes have been more intensively studied than any other aspects of the great subject of evolution, and indeed many students seem to consider "speciation" as practically synonymous with "evolution." This orientation of study has been inevitable and, in large degree, desirable. The fundamental proposition of the doctrine of special creation was the immutability of species, so that the first essential in establishing the truth of evolution was to demonstrate that one species may give rise to another. Hence the title of Darwin's great work on evolution in general, *The Origin of Species*. Variations, heredity, and processes of differentiation within species can be studied experimentally, whereas the larger features of evolution cannot. In practice, field naturalists and zoologists in museums are mainly occupied in distinguishing and examining species and their subdivisions, so much more numerous than the broader groups and so much more difficult to recognize.[10] More broadly, in dealing with recent animals, this is the best place to attack problems of evolution, where they begin, within populations and in their readily observed characteristics and activities. Here the basic theories of population genetics, partially summarized above, were worked out.

Aspects of speciation that bear essentially on our present theme, that of the general features of the history of life and the meaning of evolution, have already been discussed by implication if not explicitly. The subject has other aspects

---

[10] An excellent discussion of speciation from this particular point of view, together with copious citations from the enormous recent literature on speciation in general, is E. Mayr's *Systematics and the Origin of Species* (New York, Columbia University Press, 1944).

that are both fascinating and important, particularly the question of isolating mechanisms, the evolutionary devices for preventing interbreeding between closely related and formerly united populations. These aspects are not, however, absolutely necessary to the development of the broader subject of this book and adequate treatment of them would itself extend to book length.

One thing more may, however, be said about speciation in relationship to the processes of evolution here more extensively or explicitly treated. Speciation is the final detail, the filling up of the interstices, in the long process of packing every available environment with as much life as it can support. It must, however, be emphasized that speciation was by no means the last thing to occur in evolution. It was equally the first, for it goes on all the time, along with any other evolutionary process that may be under way. It is the basic structure of the web of life, the ever-present detail of the fabric of evolution. It is the source and the fundamental process of diversification in the forms of organisms. Its pattern is that of branching, the separation of one group of organisms from another and the distribution between them of different portions of the stock of hereditary variation.

In the actual process of descent and change in the long history of life, speciation is one of the essential patterns. Along with this, and always embodying this within them, are two other patterns of constant occurrence and major importance. One of these is the pattern of trend, progressive, oriented change under the control of adaptation. The other is the more rapid and sporadic, recurrent rather than continuous, pattern of change in adaptive type, adoption of a new and distinct way of life. In all these interwoven patterns the same evolutionary forces are at work, but they vary endlessly in intensity, in combination, and in result.

7. *The Concept of Progress in Evolution*

IT IS impossible to think in terms of history without thinking of progress. With reference to what is at the moment, or to structure and relationships outside a framework of time, the concept of progress is irrelevant or at least unobtrusive. Classic chemistry and physics were sciences without time and the idea of progress simply did not arise in connection with, say, the union of sodium and chlorine atoms in a salt molecule. Even in these relatively nonhistorical sciences the newer concepts of the space-time continuum and the transmutation of elements through the periodic system introduce time, demand a historical approach, and involve ideas of progression or retrogression.

Life is so obviously a process in time and not merely a static condition of being that this study has always to some degree involved historical concepts. Development and progression are so plainly evident in animate nature that these features deeply impressed biologists long before the grand fact of the evolution that produced them was understood. The idea of biological progress is as old as the science of biology and it was already deeply imbedded in pre-evolutionary science. Although its actual historicity and its real relationship to the flow of time were scarcely glimpsed, this concept of a progression of life from lower to higher was fundamental both in primitive theology (such as the Semitic Creation myths) and in primitive science (such as that of Aristotle), and it was taken over, more or less as a matter of course, in later pre-evolutionary biology that still stemmed, in the main, from these two sources. Evolution, revealing the development of life as an actually and materially historical process, gave meaning to these older observations and to the almost intuitive concept of progression if not, fully, of progress. The first truly general and scientific theory of evolution, that of Lamarck, had as its central feature the very ancient and previously nonevolutionary idea of a sequence of life forms from less to more perfect.

Examination of the actual record of life and of the evolutionary processes as these are now known raises such serious doubts regarding the oversimple and metaphysical concept of a pervasive perfection principle that we must reject it altogether. Yet there is, obviously, progression in the history of life, and if we are to find therein a meaning we are required to consider whether this involves anything that we can agree to call "progress," and if so, its nature and extent.

It is a childish idea—but one deeply ingrained in our thinking, especially on political and social subjects—that change *is* progress. Progression merely in the sense of succession occurs in all things, but one must be hopelessly romantic or unrealistically optimistic to think that its trend is necessarily for the good. We must define progress not merely as movement but as movement in a direction from (in some sense) worse to better, lower to higher, or imperfect to more nearly perfect. A description of what has occurred in the course of evolution will not in itself lead us to the identification of progress unless we decide beforehand that progress *must* be inherent in these changes. In sober enquiry, we have no real reason to assume, without other standards, that evolution, over-all or in any particular case, has been either for better or for worse. Progress can be identified and studied in the history of life only if we first postulate a criterion of progress or can find such a criterion in that history itself.

The criterion natural to human nature is to identify progress as increasing approximation to man and to what man holds good. The criterion is valid and necessary as regards human history, although it carries the still larger obligation of making a defensible and responsible choice among the many and often conflicting things that men have held to be good. The criterion is also perfectly valid in application to evolution in general, provided we know what we are doing. Approximation to human status is a reasonable *human* criterion of progress, just as approximation to avian status would be a valid avian criterion or to protozoan status a valid protozoan criterion. It is merely stupid for a man to apologize for being a man or to feel, as with a sense of original sin, that an anthropocentric viewpoint in science or in other fields of thought is automatically wrong. It is, however, even more stupid, and even more common among mankind, to assume that this is the *only* criterion of progress and that it has a *general* validity in evolution and not merely a validity relative to one only among a multitude of possible points of reference.

On the other hand we may find, and we will as the discussion proceeds, that criteria *not* selected with man as the point of reference still indicate that man stands high on various scales of evolutionary progress. It would then be foolish to cry "Anthropomorphism!" After all, it may be a fact that man does stand high or highest with respect to various sorts of progress in the history of life. To discount such a conclusion in advance, simply because we are ourselves involved, is certainly as anthropocentric and as unobjective as it would be to accept it simply because it is ego satisfying. The phase now seems to be passing and we can look with amazement or with condescension on the once more general attitude among scientists that a sense of values, and especially one that values our own species, is unscientific.

As a start in the enquiry, it is quickly evident that there is no criterion of progress by which progress can be considered a *universal* phenomenon of evolution. There are the cases in which change, and therefore any possible sort of progress, has been arrested except for minor and local, not progressive fluctuations. There are also few possible definitions of "progress"—I think only one, and that one not really acceptable—under which the term could be applied both to the rise of the marvelously intricate organism of a typical crustacean, such as a crab, and to the change of this organism, in connection with parasitism, to an almost formless mass of absorptive and reproductive cells. Whatever criterion you choose to adopt, you are sure to find that by it the history of life provides examples not only of progress but also of retrogression or degeneration. Progress, then, is certainly not a basic property of life common to all its manifestations. This casts further doubt (at least) on the finalist thesis, still more on the concept of a perfecting principle, but it certainly does not justify a conclusion that progress is absent in evolution. In a materialistic world the very idea of progress implies the possibility of its opposite. To find that progress is universal would certainly be far more surprising than to find that it is only occasional.

In the record of life, there seems to be only one progressive change that involves life as a whole, and not only the evolution of particular groups within the total process: a tendency for life to expand, to fill in all the available spaces in the livable environments, including those created by the process of that expansion itself. This is one possible sort of progress. Accepting it as such, it is the only one that the evidence warrants considering general in the course of evolution. Even this, although general, is not invariable. The expansion of life has not been constant and there have been points where it lost ground temporarily, at least. The general expansion may be considered in terms of the number of individual organisms, of the total bulk of living tissue, or of the gross turnover, metabolism, of substance and energy.[1] It involves all three, and increase in any one is an aspect of progress in this broadest sense.

This general expansion is only imperfectly helpful in providing a criterion of progress applicable to a particular case. Any group that has persisted and that does make up part of the sum total of existing life must be granted a share in this progress and from this point of view protozoan and man stand on a level. There are, however, different degrees of contribution to the expansion. The little sphenodon on its islands off New Zealand is certainly not contributing very much to the filling of the earth with life. Man is making a large contribution, not only in the persons of his bulky millions but also—almost uniquely among all organisms—in his vast swarm of domestic plants and animals. A criterion is also

---

[1] This last aspect, particularly, is discussed in an extremely interesting paper by A. J. Lotka, "The Law of Evolution as a Maximal Principle," *Human Biology, 17* (1945), 167–194.

provided for evolutionary movement within any given group. As one group replaces another the net total of life may or may not be changed, but by this particular criterion alone, within the history of one group, its increase in variety and abundance may be considered ipso facto progressive and its decline retrogressive. In this sense extinction is not merely the end but also the very antithesis of progress—but ultimate extinction (the inevitable fate of all life) is no sign that progress was earlier absent in the rise and history of the group. As regards direction and intensity of expansion at any one time, man is right now the most rapidly progressing organism in the world. The actual bulk of material incorporated in *Homo sapiens* seems now quite clearly—and from other points of view, most unfortunately—to be increasing more rapidly than in any other species.

In the search for, as nearly as may be, objective criteria of progress applicable to a particular case and yet widely valid, such considerations lead to the criterion of dominance, which has been stressed almost to the exclusion of any other by the leading student of the subject, Huxley.[2] We have seen how throughout the history of life each group has tended to expand and to have one or more periods when it was particularly abundant and varied. We have seen, too, how at any given time certain groups tended to be much more varied and abundant than others, in other words to dominate the life scene, and that there has been a succession in these dominant groups. It is this succession that provides a criterion, though plainly not the only one, of evolutionary progress. Thus among the aquatic vertebrates, "fishes" (see fig. 3), it is fully justified, as long as we keep in mind the particular *kind* of progress that we mean, to say that successive dominance of Agnatha, Placodermi, and Osteichthyes represents progress and that Osteichthyes are the highest, Agnatha the lowest, group among the three. It is worthy of note, in passing, that the Chondrichthyes are generally admitted in this sequence as higher than Placodermi but lower than Osteichthyes, yet the Chondrichthyes by *this* criterion are really neither lower nor higher than the Osteichthyes. The same sort of sequence applies in the successive dominance of Amphibia, Reptilia, and Mammalia.

We do not, however, find successive dominance between,

[2] Throughout this chapter I am deeply indebted to his various profound and extended treatments of the subject even though I do not always exactly agree with him. Not only in this chapter but throughout this book I am especially indebted to *Evolution. The Modern Synthesis*, a work so rich in details that it is sometimes hard to disentangle the principles and one with a relative weakness on the historical side of the study of life, but still the best single and general statement now available on the modern theory of evolution, which should be read by everyone interested in this subject.

say Osteichthyes, Aves, and Mammalia. All three are dominant at the same time, during the Cenozoic and down to now. Taking the animal kingdom as whole, it is clearly necessary to add insects, molluscs, and also the "lowly" Protozoa as groups now dominant. (Figure 2.) If one group had to be picked as most dominant now, it would have to be the insects, but the fact is that all these groups are fully dominant, each in a different sphere. The conclusion is emphasized by cases like that of the Osteichthyes and the Amphibia—the Osteichthyes were dominant later. If this criterion were really given general validity and were objectively applied, it would be necessary to conclude that bony fishes are higher forms of life and represent a further degree of progress than amphibians, or than reptiles, for that matter.

It is true, as Huxley says, that "biologists are in substantial agreement as to what were and what were not dominant groups" and that they usually arrange these as if they constituted a single succession symbolized by the stereotyped "Age of Invertebrates," "Age of Fishes," "Age of Amphibians," "Age of Reptiles," "Age of Mammals," and "Age of Man." The fact is that such a sequence does not follow a single or a wholly objective criterion. It is not based solely, or even in the main, on the objective facts of dominance in the history of life. Two other criteria have been sneaked in: that of ancestral and descendant relationship, which is an objective and general criterion but an entirely different matter from dominance, and that of approximation to man, which also has nothing to do with the facts of dominance and which, although perfectly all right as long as we know what we are doing and do not think we are following a general and objective criterion, is specific to a single point of reference and subjective to that point, i.e., man.

The criterion of dominance is not invalidated by the fact that it does not yield a single sequence for progress in evolution. That there is or should be a single sequence was a fallacy of the pre-evolutionary perfecting principle idea and this can be a required condition of progress only when progress is defined with reference to a point and not as a general principle. Of course even as a general principle it *might* have been found that progress was a one-line affair, and should be if there were anything in most vitalist or finalist contentions, but as a matter of fact this does not turn out to be the case with the criterion of dominance or, as will be found, with any other criterion *except* that of approximation to some specific type such as man.

The various different lines of progress that are involved in successive dominance are defined by adaptive types or corresponding ways of life. Thus there is broadly one for aquatic vertebrates and broadly another, quite distinct from this, for terrestrial vertebrates, with bony fishes at the top in the former and mammals simultaneously at the top in the latter. Within each of these groups there are other, more closely circumscribed ways of life and corresponding lines of dominance and of progress (in this sense) for each of these. Among the bony fishes, there are separate lines for marine and freshwater fishes, for shallow and deep sea fishes, and so on.

In relationship to man, not taking him as point of reference but adhering to strict dominance as objective criterion, we find that he is a member of a progressive group, and generally of the most progressive, in each of the various dominance sequences in which he can properly be placed. (His dominance cannot be compared with that of molluscs or insects, for instance, because the ways of life and corresponding dominance sequences are grossly different.) A major category might be that of self-propelled, unattached organisms of medium to large size: vertebrates are dominant here; man is a vertebrate. Among these, terrestrial forms subdivide the major way of life: mammals dominant; man a mammal. Among land mammals as a whole, rodents are now clearly and strongly dominant, but within the Mammalia man belongs definitely to a dominance sequence quite different from that of the rodents and in this sequence he has recently and decisively risen to dominance. This criterion gives no justification for considering man the highest among all the forms of life, but it places him at least among the highest in his own general and particular sphere, and that is as far as the criterion can go.

This sort of succession of dominance within particular spheres, environmental and adaptive, suggests as another possible criterion of progress the successive invasion and development of these spheres. The succession is, again, multiple and does not give a single line of progress for all of evolution even if combined with dominance within each sphere. After early, multiple, basic, adaptive successions in the water, a major step here was spread of life from water to land, a step which tremendously increased the amount of life in the world and can be related to progress in the most general of all features of evolution, the total expansion of life. The step did not take place all at once or through a single group of organisms; the lines are multiple, but for each this step is from lower to higher by this particular criterion. By this criterion, too, man is a high type of animal, for his general environment was among the last to be filled by life. It really is legitimate to go beyond this and to point out that man's particular adaptive type was the latest to be developed up to now in the history of life, one radically new, never before exemplified, and with extreme potentialities for expansion. In the spreading sequence of adaptive types there is thus a criterion that seems quite definitely to place man at the top, as the highest type of organism in this particular respect.

Replacement within adaptive zones is another possible objective criterion of progress, but one that seems rather equivocal in spite of glib generalizations as to "higher" types continually replacing "lower." When replacement does occur, there seems to be pragmatic evidence that the successful group is somehow better. Presumably the "better" often or usually means improved adaptation of some sort, a special case of another and different possible concept of progress as moving toward better adaptation. The criterion of replacement is not generally applicable, and its bearing is more than dubious when, as has happened repeatedly, replacement is delayed or is successive without actual competition. The criterion does not apply to man, who, as just pointed out, is not a replacing form but one developing a totally new adaptive type.

The concept of progress as involving improvement in adaptation is rather obvious and apparently promising, for certainly adaptation and changes in it are among the most nearly universal features of evolution; but on closer examination it seems to be quite limited as a criterion for progress and of little significance in an attempt to establish any very general idea of progress in evolution. It is another criterion that gives multiple progressive sequences, and a really excessive number of these. Every organism is adapted to some particular way of life. This has always been true and always will be. Evolution does not proceed from the general to the particular but from the particular to the particular, building up and filling in the general as it goes. On the basis of adaptation alone there is no reason to consider one adaptive type higher or lower than another. Diversity of adaptive types has increased. This is the expansion and succession already discussed—but there is no way to decide that one adaptive type is more adaptive than another.

Within each of the myriads of distinct adaptive types there is a possibility for improvement in efficiency and for sharpening of the adaptation, narrowing its scope. In evolution this is the widespread phenomenon of increasing specialization. This, too, is progress of a sort and if we care to define it so; at least, it is a very frequent occurrence in evolution, one that is progressive in the sense of succession and trend, and one that does tend, on the whole, to increase the total of life, as summed over all its various lines. If we feel intuitively that specialization is not *real* progress, it is mainly because this is not the line our ancestry took and because it so often leads to extinction. Extinction is nonprogress, to be sure, but it may be preceded by progress, and specialization is an essential feature of the expansion of life which can hardly be denied the name of progress if progress be considered a possibility in evolution. Specialization is a form of evolutionary progress, one of many and one distinctive and peculiar in its aspects.

The peculiarity of progress in specialization resides mainly in its inverse relationship to the possibility of further progress. Change toward increased specialization approaches a limit and tends in general to decrease the possibility of change in any other direction, although the relationship is not rigid or invariable. Now the possibility of further progress is one criterion that cannot effectively be used to define progress going on or accomplished in the past. If potentiality for further advance were a sign of progress, then of course the first living molecule was the most progressive thing that ever lived! This is absurd, and so is the commonly stated conclusion that specialization is not "real" progress because it limits further progress. Yet progress that does not narrow, or that broadens, the chances of further progress is evidently a different thing from progress that is self-limiting, as specialization often is. The difference becomes important only in connection with an actual movement of evolution that shows progress on other criteria than those of limitation or expansion of possibilities for future change.

There is a progress in adaptability which often tends to conflict with or be restricted by progress in adaptation (specialization), but which only comes into play if, in fact, further adaptation does occur and that adaptability is utilized in a way that can be considered progressive. That intricate sentence really does mean something, and the meaning is particularly significant for the human species. Our ancestors did not progress much as regards specialization. By that criterion, we stand low among mammals and indeed rather low among animals in general. This is the only criterion of progress that we have found by which man is a low type of animal. In fact in our rise there was a broadening and not a narrowing of the specificity of our adaptation. Our own activities, with the invention of clothing, tools, and the rest, have still further broadened that specificity and have placed us beyond any other organism in adaptability. The exploitation of that adaptability has occurred, and is still going on, as man adapts further not to one but to a great variety of ways of life. This is progress of a sort and to a degree altogether unique in the history of life.

This development is often expressed as, or I might say "confused with," progressive independence from the environment. It is rather the ability to cope with a greater variety of environments than lessening of dependence on environment as a whole, and the distinction seems real and important. It is also something peculiarly human in its ·degree and even, in considerable part, in its kind and so must be suspect as a human and not a general or objective criterion of progress in evolution as a whole. The nonhuman example most often given for progress as increasing independence from the environment is the freeing of the amphibians from dependence on water as a living medium and then of the reptiles from dependence on water in which to lay their eggs. It has been remarkably overlooked that this was only an exchange and not a loss of dependency. The reptile finally became completely dependent on dry land—and water is much more widespread!

Control over the environment is still more clearly progress if we agree to consider progress frankly as defined from the human position. At least it leads us to the position that only man is really progressive in the history of life. Actual *control* of environment, as opposed to the ability merely to move about in search of suitable environments, means of escape from unsuitable ones, or the ability to get along in varied and varying environments, is almost exclusively a human ability. Such things as beaver dams are negligible in comparison and they are isolated marvels in the animal kingdom that will hardly be considered as criteria for evolutionary progress without reference to man. Means of *protection* from the environment are practically universal among organisms, although they vary greatly in nature. They may exemplify progress, on some other standard, but they do not help particularly to define it. The fact that control of environment is so nearly exclusive to man does not mean that it is not progress, but only that it is a peculiarly *human* sort of progress, part of the larger wonder that man is a new sort of animal that has discovered new possibilities in ways of life—and this is progress whether referred specifically to the human viewpoint or not.

However progress may be defined among such broader ways as have now been exemplified, there are accompanying structural and physiological changes that constitute the concrete concomitants of such more abstract progress or that are the material means by which progress occurs.

Increasing structural complication at once comes to mind, especially as evolution has so often and so misleadingly been generalized as just a succession from simple to more complex forms of life. This was an aspect of progress, and an important one, far back in the days of fundamental progress in successive occupation of the major and more radically different ways of life. The first step in this beyond the protozoans was the rise of many-celled animals, which was progress involving complication of structure. Complication was also markedly involved in the rise of the diverse multicellular phyla, but again we find that this was progress in multiple lines, not a single process of increasing complication nor even a central line with branching blind alleys that might or might not be progressive in this respect. In a broad way complication was involved in successive spread to new spheres of life, and higher forms, by any acceptable criterion, are on the whole more complex than lower; but within this broad picture correlation of complication and progress becomes quite irrelevant as regards particular cases. It would be a brave anatomist who would attempt to prove that Recent man is more complicated than a Devonian jawless fish. Perhaps he is, but I do not know just how you would set about proving it (other than by rigging your definition of "complication"), or what it would mean if you did prove it. Yet everyone will agree, by any acceptable definition of "progress" whatsoever, that man has progressed a great deal further than the jawless fish had.

As a matter of fact within such groups as show, for instance, the phenomenon of successive dominance, it is at least as usual for progress (by the criterion of dominance, for example) to be accompanied by structural simplification as by complication. This observation is the basis of "Williston's law." [3] As Williston, one of the great American vertebrate paleontologists, phrased it, "The parts in an organism tend toward reduction in number, with the fewer parts greatly specialized in function." This sort of change is, on the whole, in the direction of simplification rather than complication. It is so, at least, to the extent that reduction in number of parts is a simplification. Of course the specialization of remaining parts, as these become fewer, may complicate their individual structure, but there is no constancy in this. The teeth of cats, for instance, have become fewer and the remaining teeth have become greatly specialized in function, but these specialized teeth are considerably simpler in form than were the corresponding teeth of Paleocene carnivores.

The "law" applies in many sequences that show progress under any usual definition and this shows that progressive simplification, as well as progressive complication, may accompany progress. (It would not be valid in either case to say that

---

[3] Such a "law" is, of course, really just a description of what is observed to happen as a rule, or at least with some frequency, in evolution.

such a change *constitutes* progress.) Such apparent contradiction as exists here disappears when the "law" is related to function, a fact that seems not to have been very clearly brought out in morphological evolutionary studies seeking to generalize the phenomena of structural change without reference to function. Williston's "law" is followed *only* when multiple parts combine to perform the same or closely related functions. The fewer parts continue to perform these same functions, or more specialized functions evolved from these. This particular sort of structural reduction therefore does not represent reduction in function, which is usually retrogressive and not in the direction of progress. A familiar example of this process is found in the multiple legs of the earliest crustaceans (trilobites), all performing the function of locomotion, and the many fewer legs of a modern crab, some of which perform the same function of locomotion and some the specialized function of grasping. (See fig. 22.) The very common reduction in numbers of teeth and of skeletal parts in vertebrates also occurs, as a rule, in accordance with this "law" and its limitations.[4]

Another group of features involved in progressive evolution and often but incorrectly used as criteria of progress arises from the ancestral-descendant relationship and relative degrees

Trilobite

Crab

Fig. 22. An example of "Williston's law" (see text). The trilobite, an ancient crustacean, had many similar segments and legs. The crab, a living crustacean, has relatively few and dissimilar segments and legs. (Data for the trilobite from Raymond.)

of difference from a common ancestor. It has been noted that the claimed dominance sequence invertebrate—fish—amphib-

---

[4] The subject has been well discussed and details of the example of reduction in number of skull bones given by W. K. Gregory in " 'Williston's Law' Relating to the Evolution of Skull Bones in the Vertebrates" (*Amer. Jour. Physical Anthropology,* 20 [1935], 123–152).

ian—reptile—mammal—man is *not* arranged in the objective
order of dominance but in the ancestral-descendant sequence
oriented with respect to man. To suppose that older groups
are ipso facto lower on the scale of progress than younger
groups, or ancestors than their descendants, or among contemporaries those more like the common ancestor than those
less like, is to confuse change with progress. These differences
denote change, no more and no less. In themselves they give
no clue or criterion as to whether that change has been in the
direction of progress. Of course if progress *has* occurred in
the given case—something that has to be decided on other
grounds altogether—*then* the older group will be lower than
the younger and the ancestor than the descendant and then
the amount of change from a common ancestor will reflect
the amount of progress made by its various descendants.

The limitations and applications of such changes as are involved in progressive complication of structure or in Williston's "law" strongly suggest that the concomitants of evolutionary progress should be sought in function and in structure
as related plainly to function and not in the morphogenetic
principles and "laws," so dear to the heart of the paleontologist, which are expressed in terms of primarily structural
change. A change that seems often to be involved in progress,
although evidently not perfectly correlated with it, is increase
in the general energy or maintained level of vital processes.[5]
This is rather vague, but it is easy to find concrete examples.
A good one occurs in the transition from reptiles to mammals,
which was clearly in the direction of evolutionary progress by
most definitions. The metabolic system of reptiles has a low
vital minimum above which it can rise for bursts of quick but
not of sustained energy, and its action is rather closely circumscribed by external conditions. The mammalian system
(typically) has a higher vital minimum which is maintained
at almost constant level and from which can be developed not
only quick but also extraordinarily sustained energy expendi-
tures. Many structural changes are correlated with this. For
instance, the mammalian system requires effective utilization
of a more constant food supply, and this in turn has been
achieved by changes in the digestive system and in the means
of obtaining food, including the teeth and jaws.

With regard to energy level, mammals as a whole stand near
but not quite at the top among animals; among vertebrates,
the birds exceed them, but mammals and birds do not belong
in the same logical progress sequence by most criteria. There

[5] This is particularly emphasized in A. N. Sewertzoff's important work, *Morpho-
logische Gesetzmässigkeiten der Evolution* (Jena, Gustav Fischer, 1931), which
also contains a great wealth of material on other progressive features of evolution
and on its oriented aspects.

has been some, but not much or constant, progression in this respect within the Mammalia. Man is simply a typical mammal as far as general vital energy and its maintenance are concerned, which is to say that he stands very high among animals in general.

This particular change has carried with it other concomitants some of which are related to other rather general functional progressions. Perhaps the most important of these has to do with reproduction and care of the young. There is a sequence from mere emission of eggs and sperm into the environment, so that even mating is external and at random, through internal fertilization, to various degrees of care for the fertilized eggs until the young are born, and finally to postnatal care for the young. The sequence, or parts of it in a great variety of forms, occur in numerous different evolutionary lines which are progressive, by most different definitions of that term. It reaches a very high development among birds, which are able by their constant and high body temperature to provide a nearly uniform and favorable environment for the developing egg and which provide considerable postnatal care to the young. The mammals are, however, the highest animals in this particular respect and the case is clear-cut and indisputable, from the protection and uniformity of internal gestation through most highly perfected postnatal care including provision of nearly uniform and highly nutritious food from the mother. Man has added to this the longest and most elaborate postnatal care among the mammals and so, in this sequence, is decisively the highest of all animals.

Reproductive method is particularly closely related to natural selection, which is differential reproduction, and progression in this respect has far-reaching evolutionary consequences beyond the more immediate fact that it makes production and survival of the young increasingly certain. Internal fertilization makes possible choice of mate and introduces a new and important adjunct of natural selection. Care of the developing egg and provision of increasingly constant environmental conditions for it minimize environmentally induced variation, which is not hereditary and not directly subject to control by natural selection, and present for such control variations more strictly hereditary. Postnatal care of the young leads (even in non-humans) to education and to a new sort of heredity, the transmission of learning, which again reaches a unique level in man.

Another and probably even more important element in many lines and sorts of evolutionary progress has been "change in the direction of increase in the range and variety of adjustments of the organism to its environment," as Herrick has put it.[6] Note well that this is not at all the same thing as "increased control over and independence of the environment." It is increased awareness and perception of the environment and increased ability to react accordingly. (I know that some students of the subject deny that any animals below man, or certainly the really lowly types, are "aware" or "perceive" anything whatsoever; for the present purpose, this does not matter in the least; all animals *act* as if they had awareness and perception—even the ameba does.) The progressive trend is to gather more and different kinds of information about the environment in which the organisms do, in fact, exist and to develop apparatus for appropriate adjustments in accordance with this information. On lowest levels this involves only diffuse sensibility and reactability to such signals from the environment as do have an effect on any protoplasm: some types of radiation, motion and bodily contact, temperature, and chemical effects. At higher levels it involves very complex and specialized sensory organs and equally or more complex nervous systems and other coordinating mechanisms.

Earlier discussion of photoreceptors (in Chapter 4) has already exemplified the kind of structural progression that may be associated with this sort of functional advance. It showed, too, how progress may be multiple and not in one line or toward a single type of perfected sense organ, even when the environmental signals to be received are all of the same sort. Environments differ in the stimuli that are present, and the usefulness of sensations of various sorts also differs in different ways of life even within what is, otherwise, the same environment. Thus the lateral line organs of fishes, which are receptors for variations in pressure or movement in a surrounding liquid medium, are lost in terrestrial animals which do not live in such a medium, but the related ear mechanism is adapted for reception of rhythmic pressure variations (sounds) in air. This mechanism shows marked progress, and in general there is progress, eventually very great, in the central control and reacting mechanisms. Pit vipers, although they live in environments similar to those of other snakes and broadly of many other terrestrial vertebrates, have in the pits for which they are named a special sense organ which is a directional receptor for low degrees of heat radiation, a mechanism found in no other animals. The apparatus detects the body heat of small mammals on which these vipers live. This peculiar development certainly counts as progress in perception (and the appropriate reactions are

[6] In a very short note which is worth many pages of less pithy discussion, including, I fear, the present pages: C. J. Herrick, "Progressive Evolution" (*Science, 104* [1946], 469).

also there, of course), but the absence of such an apparatus has no relevance to progress in animals that do not live on warm-blooded prey or that have other, equally or more efficient means of locating such prey.

This sort of progress, with its innumerable different degrees and many different lines of progression, is more widespread and also more fundamental than such features as independence or control of environment. It is, indeed, progress in perception of and reaction to environment that underlies and makes possible such quite limited degrees of independence and control as have been achieved. It is also evident that this concept of progress is not man-centered but provides a general criterion applicable without necessary reference to the human condition. As a matter of fact, when the criterion is applied to man, it is another that places him at the highest level of evolutionary progress. No organism has receptors and analyzers for all possible signals from the environment, or for more than a small fraction of these. For the stimuli actually present in his environment man has about as good a set of receptors as any animal. His associated perceptual, coordinating, and reacting apparatus is incomparably the best ever evolved. Moreover in the new sort of evolution so characteristic of man, that of social structure and transmitted learning, man has supplemented his organic receptors with external, inorganic receptors of a range and delicacy unknown to any other animal—such as the radio, to mention only the most familiar of many examples.

Progress in awareness and reactibility to more numerous degrees and more different kinds of environmental stimuli is linked with adaptability and often carries with it progress in individual versatility. This increase in the possible range and variety of reactions by the individual organism makes each more independent as a unit and more distinctive in its particular reactions and interrelationships. There may be, in short, an accompanying progress in individualization. This, too, is widespread in the various evolutionary lines among animals, although like other sorts of progress it is far from universal. (The virtual absence of progressive awareness in plants can be directly related to their relative lack of individualization.) Everyone has noticed that a mammal or a bird is much more individualized than, say, an oyster, not in structure or appearance, which may be more varied and more distinctive of the individual among oysters than among mammals or birds, but in reaction patterns, behavior, or general ability. Progress in versatilization of the individual and in individualization within the species has been carried by human evolution to altogether new heights. Individualization is a prerequisite for the human type of socialization and finds in the latter opportunity for its greatest possible development— an apparent paradox that is, in fact, readily resolved and has the greatest importance in understanding of man's evolutionary status, a subject to be discussed in the last chapters of this book.

In summary, evolution is not invariably accompanied by progress, nor does it really seem to be characterized by progress as an essential feature. Progress has occurred within it but is not of its essence. Aside from the broad tendency for the expansion of life, which is also inconstant, there is no sense in which it can be said that evolution *is* progress. Within the framework of the evolutionary history of life there have been not one but many different sorts of progress. Each sort appears not with one single line or even with one central but branching line throughout the course of evolution, but separately in many different lines. These phenomena seem fully consistent with, and indeed readily explained by, the materialistic theory of evolution sketched in the last chapter. They are certainly inconsistent with the existence of a supernal perfecting principle, with the concept of a goal in evolution, or with control of evolution by autonomous factors, a vital principle common to all forms of life.

Among many possible definitions of progress, and many corresponding sorts of progress in evolution, that of change toward a particular sort of organism is as valid as any other as long as it is clearly understood to be specific with respect to a selected point and subjective in this sense. To man, evolutionary change in the direction of man *is* progress, of this particular sort. It is not progress in a general or objective sense and does not warrant choice of the line of man's ancestry as the central line of evolution as a whole. More general and objective criteria of progress are available and corresponding sorts of progress exist in the history of life. These, too, fail to designate man's ancestry as a central line, and indeed fail to reveal any one such line. A majority of them do, however, show that man is among the highest products of evolution and a balance of them warrants the conclusion that man is, on the whole but not in every single respect, the pinnacle so far of evolutionary progress.

8. Historical Retrospect: the Evolution of Evolution

MAN'S attempts to understand the history of life have had an evolution of their own, an intellectual evolution in which progress toward truth and comprehension has been, if not constant, at least continual. The history of this progress casts light on the meaning of evolution to man. Consideration of successive contributions and of rejected alternatives shows not only how the current understanding of evolution and of man's place in it was achieved but also why and with what degree of confidence the present views on these subjects are to be received. Such consideration, necessarily summary, is the remaining necessity before turning to the final phase of this enquiry, examination of the philosophical and ethical implications of all that has gone before.

The Greeks, especially Anaximander, Empedocles, and Aristotle in, respectively, the sixth, fifth, and fourth centuries B.C., are usually credited with the first major strides toward comprehension of the history of life and specifically toward discovery of the truth of evolution. They will not long detain us here because, as a matter of fact, their contribution in this particular respect was almost negligible. They, or at least Aristotle, made great progress in the description of nature but little in the understanding of it, and indeed on the whole they placed impediments in the way of this. Aside from some speculations quite on a par with the primitive myth and magic of savages—who widely hold beliefs that contain the germs of evolutionary ideas—the most nearly historical biological concept reached by the Greek philosophers was that of a progression of organic forms, as abstract types, from lowest and simplest to highest and most complex (man, of course). The concept was idealistic and essentially nonhistorical, for it was not related to the realistic and historical facts of organic descent through successive generations.

This metaphysical attempt at explanation of the nature and diversity of the forms of life crystallized as dogma and was the most serious obstacle in the way of inductive and truly scientific study of life for many centuries. The idealistic progression was interpreted theologically as the pattern of creation and its realistic manifestation as the static result of special creation by God of each kind of living thing as it now exists. In the light of the extremely limited knowledge of life

124

processes prior to about the seventeenth century and practically complete ignorance of the rock record of the history of the earth, this was a reasonable hypothesis and could be considered as such from the scientific as well as from the theological point of view. In retrospect it seems entirely obvious that there was an equally reasonable alternative hypothesis, that the progression was an idealization of a material historical sequence. It even seems that there was really no legitimate theological issue at stake, for creation according to static pattern is neither more nor less theistic than creation by historical process and the two could, and can, about equally well be accommodated to revelation and to what is really essential in Christian or other religious dogma.

The hypothesis of special creation did, nevertheless, become so deeply involved in Christian belief that it was felt to be essential to that belief, and still is by a considerable proportion of Christians. Thus in the viewpoint of the church and in the emotions of its members it could not be considered as a hypothesis at all, subject to investigation and verification and to consideration of alternative hypotheses on the same basis. To accept such a view would have threatened the emotional and not infrequently also the economic security of the true believers. In such an atmosphere conscious formulation of the otherwise so obvious alternative hypothesis was subjected to psychological repression in the individual, and if it had risen to consciousness its open expression would have been subjected to still fiercer social repression. In fact no such expression was made during the first fifteen centuries of the Christian era.

It is hard to believe that no solitary thinker ever thought of the historical hypothesis during this long time when the truth, far from prevailing, had no chance for expression or serious consideration. That such lonely gropings may have occurred is suggested by some evidence that sub rosa consideration of the historical hypothesis may have been rather widespread in the seventeenth century, when the psychological and social sanctions against it were beginning to relax, although still strong enough to prevent fully overt consideration of this topic. There are, for instance, definite but timid hints in the works of Descartes (who died in 1650) that he privately held evolutionary views. More open statement was suppressed by "distaste for hell-fire and respect for the church." [1]

The subject was about to break into the open, not as an opposing dogma or an anticlerical movement, but as a possibility regarding the facts of existence on the earth subject to

[1] A summarized explanation of Descartes' determination not to publish any of his scientific discoveries as given in the analytical table of contents of E. T. Bell, *Men of Mathematics* (New York, Simon and Schuster, 1937).

human investigation and eventual decision. The honorable list of the pioneers who finally gave it this status would be too long here, but some names must not be omitted: Hooke (1635-1703), Ray (1627-1705), de Maillet (1656-1738), Maupertuis (1698-1759), Buffon (1707-88), and Erasmus Darwin (1731-1802, grandfather of Charles). All of these openly considered evolution as a possibility and most of them proclaimed it as a reality. They were, however, unable to produce from the still scanty store of facts then available sufficient weight of evidence to overcome the inertia of centuries and the almost unanimous opposition of theologians, whose grounds were not scientific and are therefore not hereafter pertinent to the history of evolutionary science. They also failed to produce a general and consistent theory as to *how* evolution works (which, of course, is quite a different matter from *whether* it works), although they had ideas on this subject which sometimes—as later was found—came close to the mark.

Lamarck (1744-1829) holds a place in the history of evolutionary theory second only to that of Darwin, for he explicitly concluded that evolution is a general fact embracing every form of life in a single historical process and he proposed an inclusive theory as to how this process works. It happens that his theory did not stand up in the light of later knowledge and no one follows it today, not even the very few remaining students who call themselves "neo-Lamarckians." It was, nevertheless, a brave attempt and more than that, for it paved the way for later study and it indicated crucial lines of attack which did finally lead to success. Lamarck took over, as was practically inevitable, the old idea that all the forms of life represent a progression with man as its highest form. He was, however, too well acquainted with existing plants and animals and too little blinded by tradition to fail to notice that this is not really true. He therefore concluded that although this progression is the major feature of evolution and its principal cause (but the progression's cause not specified), it is perturbed and does not work out regularly because of local adaptation to so many different ways of life. Adaptation he supposed to be brought about by the habits of animals. The environment would require habits appropriate to it, the habits would produce structural changes from use or disuse of the various organs, and these changes would be inherited.

We know now that changes arising from habits cannot be inherited, except in the quite different and characteristically human inheritance of learning, and that there is no such thing as the old Aristotelian single progression from simple and imperfect to complex and perfect. Yet Lamarck observed, more clearly than many of his successors, that evolution involves both oriented and random features and that both must be explained in a consistent general theory. He also focused attention on adaptation, an evident and universal fact in nature, as the prime problem that *must* be faced in any attempt to explain evolution. This was all the more true in Lamarck's day and through Darwin's generation because the then numerous supporters of special creation as a scientific theory, not as dogma or divine revelation, all pointed to adaptation as the one unanswerable argument in favor of their view.

It is not, then, surprising that the main theme of the work of Charles Darwin (1809 [2]-82) was not establishment of the truth of evolution, although he did that too, but an attempt to explain adaptation and to erect a general theory of evolution on the basis of this explanation of adaptation. Darwin's whole theory, in its final development at his own hands, involved four major factors which were, in order of his opinion as to their decreasing importance: natural selection, inherited effects of use and disuse (as suggested by Lamarck), likewise inherited direct action on the organism by external conditions (a factor denied by Lamarck but emphasized by his also pre-Darwinian successor St. Hilaire), and finally, "variations which seem to us in our ignorance to arise spontaneously." Of these, natural selection is particularly associated with Darwin's name to such an extent that it is commonly supposed to be the whole of the Darwinian theory, of which it was the most important but not the only part. Adaptation was explained in the main by natural selection, as it still is.

Darwin was one of history's towering geniuses and ranks with the greatest heroes of man's intellectual progress. He deserves this place first of all because he finally and definitely established evolution as a fact, no longer a speculation or an alternative hypothesis for scientific investigation. His second greatest achievement was correct identification of a major element in the rise of adaptation: natural selection. It must, however, be noted that the modern concept of natural selection has been considerably broadened and refined and is not quite the same as Darwin's. He recognized the fact that natural selection operated by differential reproduction, but he did not equate the two. In the modern theory natural selection is differential reproduction, plus the complex interplay in such reproduction of heredity, genetic variation, and all the other factors that affect selection and determine its results. In the Darwinian system, natural selection was elimination, death,

[2] Here is an interesting coincidence that I have long cherished, not because it means anything but because it permits remembrance of three important dates for the price of one: Lamarck's most important work, the *Philosophie zoologique*, was published in the year of Darwin's birth, and Charles Darwin and Abraham Lincoln were born on the same day.

of the unfit and survival of the fit in a struggle for existence, a process included in natural selection as it is now known but not forming all or even the major part of that process.

Darwin's views as to the operation of evolution had other deficiencies which were flaws not in his genius but in the knowledge of his time. Chief among these was almost complete ignorance of how heredity actually operates and how hereditary variations arise. This and the limited view of natural selection as involving only the death or survival of individuals whose variations were taken as given, raised some doubt as to whether his theory really accounted for the *origin* of species and not merely for the elimination of some variations. His explanation of adaptation also came under fire with two oddly contrasting arguments: it was said on one hand that adaptation is too universal and too refined in detail to be accounted for by mere weeding out among random variations, and on the other hand that adaptation is not universal enough and that nonadaptive, still more inadaptive, characteristics should have been weeded out if natural selection were really an evolutionary factor. In other words, it was insisted that evolution should be all random or all oriented, and the observed mixture of the two seemed inexplicable or at least unexplained.

While Darwin's demonstration that evolution *has* occurred was encountering the inevitable attacks based on prejudice, emotion, and dogma, his theory as to *how* it occurred was thus also attacked by fellow evolutionists and on properly scientific grounds. An opposing school developed, based essentially on the universality of adaptation and the extremely intimate and pervasive relationship between structure, function, and environment. It was felt, although the necessity was never really logical, that this *must* imply a direct and causal relationship among the three. Exponents of this view (prominent among whom were the French Giard, 1846-1908, and the American Cope, 1840-97) took the second and third elements in Darwin's theory, eliminating the rest, especially natural selection, and developed them into an antithetical theory which, peculiarly, became known as neo-Lamarckian. The designation is peculiar because their theory altogether omitted the central point of Lamarck's views, that of a general perfecting tendency in evolution, and particularly stressed direct action of the environment on organic structure, which was explicitly denied by Lamarck. They did, however, also include effects of use and disuse, which had been emphasized by Lamarck and, among others, by Erasmus Darwin before him and to less degree by Charles Darwin after him. This theory, like the one that was truly Lamarckian, is now a historical curiosity in scientific, as opposed to certain ideological, circles.[3] Unsatisfactory in many minor particulars, the theory had one major and vital error: it assumed that acquired characters, those induced by environment and habit, are inherited in kind. This assumption was universal in the nineteenth century; Darwin also accepted it without serious question. It was, however, false, as was quickly and conclusively proved with the rise of the young, still new science of genetics. Without this basis, the neo-Lamarckian theory cannot possibly work.

Although now defunct, this theory had a strong influence on further progress in the study of evolution and contributed significantly to present understanding of the subject. Its emphasis on the relationship of structure-function-environment brought out a wealth of pertinent facts and made plain that the forces of evolution must effectively integrate the three. It also made evident some serious defects in Darwin's theory that further progress in knowledge had to eliminate and it particularly exposed the untenability of the extreme position taken by some of Darwin's followers, the neo-Darwinians.

The neo-Darwinians, centering especially around Weismann (1834-1914), out-Darwined Darwin. They rejected all of Darwin's own theory except its principal element, natural selection (in the strictly Darwinian, not the modern sense), and claimed this as essentially the whole process of evolution. In so doing they piled up much further evidence that natural selection does, in fact, operate and acquired considerable new insight into how it operates. They thus helped greatly to lay the firm basis on which rests our present knowledge of evolution. But by taking such a narrow, almost ridiculously oversimple view of evolution, they were forced into an untenable position.

During the latter part of the nineteenth century and into the twentieth these two opposing materialist schools of evolutionary theory lambasted each other, the neo-Lamarckians demonstrating that Darwinian natural selection cannot be the whole story, the neo-Darwinians demonstrating that it must be part, at least, of the story and that acquired characters are not inherited as such. Each side, of course, had part of the truth and between them they had the whole truth almost within their grasp had they only been able to see this. Much of the trouble was that they fought on the wrong issues and asked each other the wrong questions. The correct issue on natural selection was not whether this is or is not the cause of adapta-

[3] This statement was generally true, in Soviet Russia as elsewhere, until 1948. In that year political, not scientific, action in Moscow established as "correct" communist ideology a reactionary form of neo-Lamarckism called "Michurinism." A previously obscure pseudo-scientist, Lysenko, was made high-priest of Soviet biology. The numerous previously honest and capable Soviet biologists were forced to recant, or to disappear.

tion, but how adaptation arises in the interplay of multiple forces of which Darwinian natural selection is obviously one, but obviously only one of many. Similarly the issue on inheritance of acquired characters was put in the wrong terms. Characters, as such, are not inherited, whether they be acquired characters or not. It is a series of determiners for a developmental system that is inherited. What characters result from this depends on the interplay of the inherited determiners, the activities of the organism, and the environment during development. Thus the neo-Lamarckians were right that there is a functional and causal relationship here, but the neo-Darwinians were right that its results are not inherited *as such*.

Failure to grasp the essence of these issues and failure to put together their pieces of the truth into a whole was largely caused by the fact that a large piece was still missing. This was later to be supplied by the geneticists.

In the meantime, many students of evolution who were not rabid devotees of one of these two schools or the other fell into moods of suspicion or despair. There were two main materialistic theories and you could take the proof supplied by each that the other was untenable. What, then, to do? One could gather more facts and suspend judgment as to what meaning they might eventually have. This sounds like a fine idea and it has even been hailed (following Bacon, who never succeeded in making a discovery by his famed inductive method) as the proper procedure in science. In reality, gathering facts, without a formulated reason for doing so and a pretty good idea as to what the facts may mean, is a sterile occupation and has not been the method of any important scientific advance. Indeed facts are elusive and you usually have to know what you are looking for before you can find one.

If unwilling merely to suspend judgment, one could try to find an acceptable alternative to the two main materialistic theories of evolution. The trouble with this was that both were about as much right as they were wrong and efforts to avoid them both tended merely to be all wrong. There was no real success, even partial, in this effort until the science of genetics came along and even this, as we will see, confused the issue still more before it clarified it.

Or one could throw over materialistic and causalistic theory altogether. It was in this atmosphere that most of the extremely diverse vitalistic and finalistic theories, a veritable spate of them, were advanced. In almost all of these a sense of despair or of hope, an emotion even more blinding than despair, is evident. The relatively few first-hand investigators of evolution who abandoned causalism did so, for the most part, because they despaired of finding an adequate materialistic theory and could not endure the void of having no theory at all. Others, among them a number of professional and amateur philosophers, sounded a note of hope which was often quite plainly hope of drawing meaning from something not understood or, and this is particularly striking, hope of finding that science did, after all, confirm what were in reality their intuitive or inherited and popular prejudices. This tendency to confirm prejudice accounts for the great popularity that finalist theories have sometimes enjoyed among those incompetent to judge them adequately from either a scientific or a philosophical point of view.

All these theories, vitalist, finalist, or both, involved some degree of abandonment of causalism. They did not explain evolution, but claimed that it is inexplicable and then gave a name to its inexplicability: "élan vital" (Bergson), "cellular consciousness" (Buis, under the pseudonym "Pierre-Jean"), "aristogenesis" (Osborn), "nomogenesis" (Berg), "holism" (Smuts), "hologenesis" (Rosa), "entelechy" (Driesch), "telefinalism" (du Noüy)—the list could be greatly extended. As Huxley has remarked, the vitalists' ascribing evolution to an *élan vital* no more explained the history of life than would ascribing its motion to an *élan locomotif* explain the operation of a steam engine. The finalist left explanation still further behind, for he did not render even such lip service to causality as was often made by the nonfinalistic vitalists. In many cases the finalist merely viewed the phenomena of life with the unreasoning wonder of a child and decided that they happened simply because they were *meant* to happen. In other cases, as an eminent student has remarked in a different context, "The finalist was often the man who made a liberal use of the *ignava ratio,* or lazy argument: when you failed to explain a thing by the ordinary process of causality, you could 'explain' it by reference to some purpose of nature or of its Creator." [4]

The general features of vitalist and finalist philosophy and theory have already been outlined on previous pages. Once causalism is abandoned, there are no limitations on flights of the imagination and there are about as many separate vitalist and finalist theories as there have been vitalists and finalists. A review of each of these individually would be merely tedious and is not necessary. It has been shown that although the basic propositions common to all of them are nonscientific, that is, defined as outside the limits of scientific investigation, these would necessarily involve phenomena that can be investigated. It has also been pointed out that these diagnostic phenomena

[4] P. G. Galloway, *Philosophy of Religion* (New York, Scribner, 1914).

are in fact absent in the history of life. The mere fact that vitalism and finalism do not *explain* evolution would not warrant concluding that they therefore are not true: one cannot logically exclude a priori the possibility that evolution might really be noncausalistic and inexplicable. But the fact that the history of life is flatly inconsistent with their basic propositions does warrant the conclusion that vitalism and finalism are untenable.[5]

It must be concluded that the tendency of the vitalist and finalist theories was rather to obfuscate than to advance the study of evolution. They did, nevertheless, make some contribution to this. They emphasized and firmly established the fact that evolution involves forces that are directional in nature and creative in aspect and they exposed the weaknesses of earlier attempts to identify these forces. To this extent they had an influence in the synthesis that achieved the present causalistic explanation of this particular aspect of evolution. They have also had another effect not in the advance but in the acceptance of knowledge, which should not be underestimated. To great numbers of people unlearned in the subject, the fact of evolution has been emotionally distasteful and has been rejected on this basis alone, although the rejection has often been rationalized in other terms. Vitalistic and, more particularly, finalistic theories have persuaded many of these wishful thinkers that evolution is, after all, consonant with their emotions and prejudices. For them the pill has been sugar coated. In this respect, even du Noüy's *Human Destiny*, the most popular but even within the finalist fold one of the least logical or reliable of such efforts, may have rendered a real service. The danger is that the sugar coating may be mistaken for the remedy. Any value in it will fail of realization unless it is a step in the direction of taking truth straight.

It was during the period around the turn of the century, when the conflicts of neo-Darwinism, neo-Lamarckism, vitalism, and finalism had thrown the study of evolution into great confusion, that the science of genetics was born. Even before

[5] And the previous demonstration of this fact warrants the present unfavorable review of the position of vitalism and finalism in the history of the study of evolution. Most of the literature of this subject is either ingenuous or ingenious special pleading and little of it can be recommended to a reader who may want to read a more favorable and still a judicious review. Fortunately there is one such work, although it is not available in English: L. Cuénot, *Invention et finalité en biologie* (Paris, Flammarion, 1941).

Although Cuénot here avows himself a finalist, he still retains the charm and sobriety that mark the long sequence of his earlier work. He remains critical of the various finalist theories, and he is not blind to the scientific, logical, and philosophical weaknesses of the position in which he nevertheless finds himself. The reader should, however, note and bear in mind that when Cuénot wrote this book he was evidently completely unaware of the now current materialistic theory of evolution or of any of the crucial studies on population genetics and selection that gave impetus to this. The book does not mention even his fellow Parisian leader in this field, Teissier.

the rediscovery of Mendelism, de Vries had noted the sudden and random appearance of new varieties of plants. (His plants were primroses and we now know that his new varieties arose from chromosome mutations.) He decided that this, at last, was the real basis of evolution and he generalized it in his "mutation theory," published in 1901.

Scientists often display a human failing: whenever they get hold of some new bit of truth they are inclined to decide that it is the whole truth. Thus the neo-Darwinians insisted that natural selection was the whole truth of evolution; the neo-Lamarckians held that interaction of structure-function-environment was the whole truth; the vitalists saw the whole truth in the creative aspect of life processes; and the finalists found all basic truth in the directional nature of evolution. Similarly, many of the early geneticists, although they soon learned far more about the mechanism involved, accepted de Vries' thesis and concluded that mutation was the whole truth of evolution. Mutations are random, so it was decided that evolution is random. The problem of adaptation was, in their opinion, solved by abolishing it: they proclaimed that there is no adaptation, only chance preadaptation.

Other theories had often stumbled over the fact that there is quite plainly a random element in evolution, the nature of which had been unknown. Now the mutationists had identified the source of this random element, but their theory stumbled over the fact that evolution is not wholly random. The vitalists and finalists were right in continuing to insist on this point, although they were wrong in their own overgeneralization of insisting that the directional element is universal and in maintaining that this element is inherent in life or in its goal. The mutationist discoveries were bewildering to many field naturalists and paleontologists, because they in particular were well aware that evolution *cannot* be a purely random process and that progressive adaptation certainly does occur. For a time the discoveries of the geneticists seemed only to make confusion worse confounded. Defeatism and escapism spread among many students of evolution. One very eminent vertebrate paleontologist ended a lifetime of study of evolution with the conclusion that he did not, after all, know anything about its causes; another decided in the declining years of his prolonged and exceptionally fertile studies of the subject that good and bad angels must be directing evolution!

In fact, as the geneticists' studies progressed they were providing the last major piece of the truth so long sought regarding the causes of evolution. As this went on, it naturally began to dawn on students of the subject that each of the conflicting schools of theory had part of the truth and that none had all of it. The movement began with geneticists who wondered what effect natural selection, if it should really be a guiding force in evolution, would have on the genetic factors that they had discovered in individuals and in populations. They found that it would have a profound effect and that this effect was not exactly that predicted either by the neo-Darwinians or by the mutationists. These initial successes intensely stimulated study of evolution, which quickly regained its slipping position as the focal point of all the life sciences. Students of all the different aspects of life began to unite, each contributing from his field its special bit of evolutionary fact to add to the growing synthesis. The resulting synthetic theory [6] need not here be summarized, because it is the theory already presented, in broad outlines, in the preceding chapters.

The synthetic theory has no Darwin, being in its nature the work of many different hands. To mention any of these is to be culpable of important omissions, but if only to indicate the breadth of the synthesis it may be noted that among the many contributors have been: in England, Fisher, Haldane, Huxley, Darlington, Waddington, and Ford; in the United States, Wright, Muller, Dobzhansky, Mayr, Stebbins, and myself; in Germany, Timoféeff-Ressovsky and Rensch; in the Soviet Union, Chetverykov, Dubinin, and Schmalhausen; in France, Teissier; in Italy, Buzzati-Traverso. I do not, of course, mean to say that these students all hold opinions identical in detail. Their fields of work, not to mention other personal variables, are so diverse that this would be a miracle. All, however, have made outstanding contributions to the modern synthesis and all seem to be agreed as to its most essential features.

This work has placed the study of the causes of evolution on a new firm footing and has produced a degree of agreement as to these causes never before approached. We seem at last to have a unified theory—although a complex one inevitably, as evolution itself is a complex interaction of different processes—which is capable of facing all the classic problems of the history of life and of providing a causalistic solution of each.

This is not to say that the whole mystery has been plumbed to its core or even that it ever will be. The ultimate

---

[6] The theory has often been called neo-Darwinian, even by those who have helped to develop it, because its first glimmerings arose from confrontation of the Darwinian idea of natural selection with the facts of genetics. The term is, however, a misnomer and doubly confusing in this application. The full-blown theory is quite different from Darwin's and has drawn its materials from a variety of sources largely non-Darwinian and partly anti-Darwinian. Even natural selection in this theory has a sense distinctly different, although largely developed from, the Darwinian concept of natural selection. Second, the name "neo-Darwinian" has long been applied to the school of Weismann and his followers, whose theory was radically different from the modern synthetic theory and certainly should not be confused with it under one name.

mystery is beyond the reach of scientific investigation, and probably of the human mind. There is neither need nor excuse for postulation of nonmaterial intervention in the origin of life, the rise of man, or any other part of the long history of the material cosmos. Yet the origin of that cosmos and the causal principles of its history remain unexplained and inaccessible to science. Here is hidden the First Cause sought by theology and philosophy. The First Cause is not known and I suspect that it never will be known to living man. We may, if we are so inclined, worship it in our own ways, but we certainly do not comprehend it.

Within the realm of what is clearly knowable, the main problem seems to me and many other investigators to be solved, but much still remains to be learned. Our knowledge of the material history of life is considerable, but it is only a tithe of what we should and can know. Study of the intricate dynamics of natural populations and their interrelationships is well begun, but not much more. Study of the evidently very important psychological factors in evolution seems hardly begun. In the study of individual life processes are gaps that are probably the most serious remaining in general knowledge of evolution. Precisely what is a gene and how does it act? The path to the answer is glimpsed in some recent work—that of Beadle, for instance—but the end is not yet reached. How is a genetic system translated into completed organic form? Unless this ignorance is personal, even the path to the answer is not yet really evident, as recent experimental embryology seems rather to skirt than to follow such a path.

It is to be expected that these probable future discoveries will not only greatly deepen but also modify our current ideas of evolutionary processes. It is, however, improbable that these ideas will be vitiated in an essential way. If we do not know each single step from reptilian ear to mammalian ear, we know a multitude of steps along the line. If we do not know how genetic system leads to organic system, we know that it does and we know, broadly, the equivalents in the two. Any report on scientific enquiry or on its human import will be an interim report, as long as our species lasts and continues to value truth, but in the current knowledge of evolution we have an excellent basis for such an interim report.

9. Man's Place in Nature

THE FIRST grand lesson learned from evolution was that of the unity of life. One of the great ethical achievements of early Christianity and some of the other religions was recognition, in principle, of the brotherhood of man. While it refuted certain other intuitive conclusions of various Christian and other theologians, confirmation of the truth of evolution established this doctrine as a scientific fact. It also carried the conclusion to a much higher level, one rejected by many Christian theologians (although it can be an intensification rather than a denial of basic Christian philosophy) and one glimpsed, however imperfectly, in some other religious systems. Not only are all men brothers; all living things are brothers in the very real, material sense that all have arisen from one source and been developed within the divergent intricacies of one process.

Man is part of nature and he is kin to all life. Yet the metaphoric "brotherhood," while a valid expression of the fact of essential unity, is evidently too strong a term if we consider it more literally and in greater detail. Man is related to every other organism that has existed, or that does or will exist on the earth, but it is perfectly obvious that he is more nearly related to some than to others. It is obvious that man is an animal and not a plant, which is a taxonomic way of saying that he is more closely related, not only in structural and functional resemblances but also in material origin, to all animals than to any plant. Among the animals it is equally obvious that, in the same sense, man is a vertebrate and not an invertebrate. Among vertebrates he is a mammal, not one of the various sorts of "fishes," an amphibian, a reptile, or a bird. Among mammals he is a primate, a member of the Order Primates and of no other of the numerous mammalian orders.

As the degrees of relationship are narrowed, the distinctions become less and their significance becomes less obvious. More detailed evidence is needed and its interpretation is more difficult. The general position of man within the animal kingdom, within the vertebrate subphylum, and within the mammalian class is absolutely established and beyond any doubt. His exact position within the primate order and his detailed relationship to each of the other primates, living and fossil, are at the present time approximately established but are not yet known beyond all question and with complete precision. We want and need to know these final details and certainly few subjects are more fascinating. These details have, however, no particular importance for the broad problems of philosophy and of ethics. The basis is established and all the essential questions are answered by the knowledge that all life is one and that within this vast unit man belongs to the particular subdivision known as the Order Primates. Such questions as whether *Pithecanthropus* is a direct ancestor of all, part, or none of the present mass of humanity or whether the gorilla, the tarsier, or some other living primate is the closest surviving branch from the human ancestry need not concern us here, for they really have no essential bearing on the nature of man or on man's place in nature.

The establishment of the fact that man is a primate, with all its evolutionary implications, early gave rise to fallacies for which there is no longer any excuse (and never was much) but which still sometimes affect the thinking of evolutionists and the reaction of those who have not yet faced the truth of evolution. These fallacies arise from what Julian Huxley calls "the 'nothing-but' school." [1] It was felt or said that because man is an animal, a primate, and so on, he is *nothing but* an animal or *nothing but* an ape with a few extra tricks.[2] It is a fact that man is an animal, but it is not a fact that he is nothing but an animal. (It is not a fact that man is an ape, extra tricks or no, and so, of course, all the less a fact that he is nothing but an ape.) Such statements are not only untrue but also vicious for they deliberately lead astray enquiry as to what man really is and so distort our whole comprehension of ourselves and of our proper values.

To say that man is nothing but an animal is to deny, by implication, that he has *essential* attributes other than those of all animals. This would be false as applied to any kind of animal; it is not true that a dog, a robin, an oyster, or an ameba is nothing but an animal. As applied to man the "nothing but" fallacy is more thoroughgoing than in appli-

[1] In his introduction to *Touchstone for Ethics, 1893–1943* by T. H. and J. Huxley (New York and London, Harper and Bros., 1947).

This excellent and thought-provoking book is highly pertinent throughout all of the present enquiry, and especially the following parts of it. It will be found that the conclusions on evolutionary ethics by the later Huxley have some striking differences from those here reached but are, in general, congruous and sometimes closely parallel. This degree of agreement is heartening, for our conclusions were, in fact, reached entirely independently and from different points of view beyond having a common basis in the modern synthetic theory of evolution.

[2] It is to be feared that some evolutionists made such statements mainly "pour épater les bourgeois" and must have known perfectly well that they distort the truth. Similarly some physicists have delighted in distortion of the statistical nature of some of their constructs by presenting them in such striking statements as that a kettle of water placed on the fire often enough will eventually freeze instead of boiling, although they must have realized that this simply is not true.

cation to any other sort of animal, because man is an entirely new kind of animal in ways altogether fundamental for understanding of his nature. It is important to realize that man is an animal, but it is even more important to realize that the essence of his unique nature lies precisely in those characteristics that are not shared with any other animal. His place in nature and its supreme significance to man are not defined by his animality but by his humanity.

Man has certain basic diagnostic features which set him off most sharply from any other animal and which have involved other developments not only increasing this sharp distinction but also making it what amounts to a difference in kind and not only a relative difference of degree. In the basic diagnosis of *Homo sapiens* the most important features are probably interrelated factors of intelligence, flexibility, individualization, and socialization. All four of these are features that occur rather widely in the animal kingdom as progressive developments, and all define different, but related, sorts of evolutionary progress. In man all four are carried to a degree incomparably greater than in any other sort of animal. All have as their requisite and basis the still more fundamental evolutionary progress "in the direction of increase in the range and variety of adjustments of the organism to its environment,"[3] which involves increased and improved means of perception of the environment and, particularly, of integrating, coordinating, and reacting flexibly to these perceptions.

In other respects, too, man represents an unusual or unique degree of progress in evolution, as was seen in discussion of that topic. He embodies an unusually large bulk of life substance and carries on a large share of the earth's vital metabolism. He is one of the dominant current forms of life, the latest to arise and now the only one within the particular dominance sequence to which he belongs. He early successfully replaced any potentially competing type and has occupied a sphere of life or great adaptive zone which was, historically, the most recent to be entered by animals. His particular sort of progress has not, to this point, been self-limiting and leads to no obvious future blind end. He is, on the whole, the most adaptable of animals. He is about as independent of environment as any animal, or, as it may more accurately be put, is able to get along in about as wide an environmental range as any. He is almost the only animal that really exerts any significant degree of control over the environment. His reproductive efficiency is the highest in the animal kingdom, with prenatal care at least as high as in any

[3] Herrick, *op. cit.*

other animal and postnatal care decidedly higher.

Even when viewed within the framework of the animal kingdom and judged by criteria of progress applicable to that kingdom as a whole and not peculiar to man, man is thus the highest animal. It has often been remarked (perhaps again merely "pour épater les bourgeois") that if, say, a fish were a student of evolution it would laugh at such pretensions on the part of an animal that is so clumsy in the water and that lacks such features of perfection as gills or a homocercal caudal fin. I suspect that the fish's reaction would be, instead, to marvel that there are men who question the fact that man is the highest animal. It is not beside the point to add that the "fish" that made such judgments would have to *be* a man!

Is it necessary to insist further on the validity of the anthropocentric point of view, which many scientists and philosophers affect to despise? Man *is* the highest animal. The fact that he alone is capable of making such a judgment is in itself part of the evidence that this decision is correct. And even if he were the lowest animal, the anthropocentric point of view would still be manifestly the only proper one to adopt for consideration of *his* place in the scheme of things and when seeking a guide on which to base *his* actions and his evaluations of them. (The point is again only reinforced by the absurdity of supposing that an animal lower than man, or that man if he were not in fact highest, could consider the scheme of things or seek for guidance in it.) This is not, of course, to make or to accept an apology for the centering of man's attention so blindly on his own personality in the here and now that he fails in just these ways, does not consider the whole scheme of things, and does not evaluate his actions on this basis.[4]

It is still false to conclude that man is *nothing but* the highest animal, or the most progressive product of organic evolution. He is also a fundamentally new sort of animal and one in which, although organic evolution continues on its way, a fundamentally new sort of evolution has also appeared. The basis of this new sort of evolution is a new sort of heredity, the inheritance of learning. This sort of heredity appears modestly in other mammals and even lower in the animal kingdom, but in man it has incomparably fuller development and it combines with man's other characteristics unique in degree with a result that cannot be considered unique only in degree but must also be considered unique in kind.

---

[4] It is this point that has been made solidly by the eminent historian R. L. Schuyler in his short but profound study, "Man's Greatest Illusion" (*Proc. Amer. Phil. Soc.*, 92 [1948], 46-50), although he was carried away by his thesis (and I think misled by some of the physical scientists) to the point of denying validity also to the broader anthropocentric view of the universe, to forgetting that *man* is doing the thinking and the acting, *not* the cosmos.

Organic evolution rejects acquired characters in inheritance and adaptively orients the essentially random, nonenvironmental interplay of genetical systems. The new evolution peculiar to man operates directly by the inheritance of acquired characters, of knowledge and learned activities which arise in and are continuously a part of an organismic-environmental system, that of social organization. Organic inheritance is limited in its spread in space and in time by its rigid requirements of proximity and of continuity. Learning inheritance was similarly limited in its earlier stages, and it still is in all the lower animals, not subject to the new evolution; but in modern man it has escaped these limitations. Means have been devised for recording and transmitting knowledge external to the organism, by graphic methods, at first, and now also by recordings of several other types and by wire and wireless transmission. In the new evolution we can inherit directly from ancestors dead two thousand years or from ancestors younger, perhaps, than we are and half the world away from us or from our organic kin. Our inheritance can be passed on, instantaneously or after a lapse of untold generations, to our whole species and without any necessary course of gradual spread in the population—a potentiality seldom or never now fully realized and yet surely inherent in the new heredity.[5]

Human social organization is in a sense the basis of this new evolution, but more strictly it is the medium in which the new heredity operates and an evolving result of the interactions of that heredity with many other factors, both organic and social in nature. Within the structure of the species, including, of course, the human species, organic evolution operates in habitually interbreeding groups, which are always defined in part by geographic proximity although other ecological factors also normally play a part, and which, among themselves, have varying degrees of interchange of heredity. Within the structure of society as a whole the new evolution operates in what may be called habitually interthinking groups. These also are defined in part by geographic proximity and by geographic concomitants in the social organization, notably nationality and language. Such definition is not, however, required by the nature of the new heredity, as it is by

[5] This concept of a contrast between the two sorts of evolution and the two sorts of heredity has been skillfully developed by a number of other students in recent years, among them E. W. Sinnott, "The Biological Basis of Democracy" (*Yale Review*, 35 [1945], 61–73); and C. H. Waddington, "Human Ideals and Human Progress" (*World Review* [August, 1946], pp. 29–36). There are, of course, still earlier more or less explicit statements of the same idea. It will be understood that originality is not claimed for any part of the present thesis (the truth is seldom original) and that no time has been wasted and no space used in seeking to establish meaningless priorities.

that of organic heredity. Geographic restrictions on inter-thinking are still very evident, but they could be eliminated, and in the meantime other defining factors are more prominent and more complex than in the case of interbreeding. Science, the principal mechanism for producing new hereditary materials transmitted by interthinking, has made some progress (not nearly enough) in eliminating the geographic factors. Political, religious, economic, and (in interaction with organic heredity) racial factors loom large in delimitation of interthinking groups and often override geographic delimitation although the geographic social organization of nationality has some tendency to maintain a relationship.

The new evolution is itself a result of organic evolution, but it is something essentially different in kind. Although it is semantically correct and scientifically enlightening to call both "evolution," it is extremely important to recognize that the difference in kind makes this in large part an analogy and not a straight equivalence. We may expect to find, and do find, that many general principles of evolution apply analogously to the two, but it is invalid and indeed dangerous to assume that equivalent evolutionary principles operate throughout the two and that principles discovered regarding one may forthwith be applied to interpretation of the other. Since we now know much more about organic evolution than about societal evolution, this fallacious sort of transfer is usually attempted from the field of biology to that of sociology. Examples of this will be discussed in connection with the search for a naturalistic ethic. The confusion of analogy and equivalence between the old evolution and the new lies at the root of the difficulties of that search and of some of its downright vicious outgrowths.

Organic evolution and societal evolution must, then, be not only constantly compared in their common aspects as evolution but also constantly contrasted in their differences as sharply distinct sorts of evolution. A few of the many contrasts have already been mentioned. One more, which may prove most basic of all, should be strongly emphasized. In organic evolution new factors arise as mutations without volition and without any fixed equivalence to needs or desires. Once they have arisen, their fate or further role in evolution is determinate and follows from the interplay of factors in which the organisms assist but over which they have no semblance of control. In the new evolution new factors arise as elements in consciousness, although always somehow influenced by and sometimes directly produced from the tangled psychological undergrowths of habit, emotion, and the subconscious. They arise in relationship to needs and desires of individuals and commonly in relationship to the individual's perception and judgments of the needs and desires of a social group. Once they have arisen, their further evolutionary role is not mechanistically determinate and is subjected to the influence not only of the actual needs and desires of the group and of volitions extremely complex in basis but also of an even more complex interplay of emotions, value judgments, and moral and ethical decisions.[6]

Through this very basic distinction between the old evolution and the new, the new evolution becomes subject to conscious control. Man, alone among all organisms, knows that he evolves and he alone is capable of directing his own evolution. For him evolution is no longer something that happens to the organism regardless but something in which the organism may and must take an active hand. The possibility and responsibility spread from the new evolution to the old. The accumulation of knowledge, the rise of a sense of values, and the possibility of conscious choice, all typical elements in the new evolution, also carry the means of control over organic evolution, which is determinate but is determined, in part, by factors that can be varied by the human will.

Man's control over either of these processes, even over the new evolution from which the means of control arise, is neither rigid nor boundless. He can neither make sure that evolution will certainly occur without deviation in a given direction at a given rate nor make a choice among all conceivable directions and rates. In both sorts of evolution he must still, to mention only these basic limitations, work with the changes that arise and disseminate them by existing mechanisms. In organic evolution he cannot decide what sort of mutation he would like to have and he must await the processes of differential reproduction for the integration and spread of the mutation chosen. In the social process, although the rise of new materials is conscious, their range is strongly limited at any given time. New knowledge and ideas do not and cannot come in exact accordance with our needs or wishes. Their spread and translation into action are also far from instantaneous, as we all know, and there is certainly no reason to think that this will ever depend on processes much more rapid than displacement against a great weight of inertia and active opposition. But we do not conclude that man cannot control floods because he cannot make rain fall upward. The infantile fantasy of becoming whatever we wish as fast

---

[6] For present purposes I have assumed that some measure of free will and choice is consistent with historical (not necessarily mechanistic) determinism. The assumption is a large one and philosophically disputable, yet it does have justification and it cannot be discussed further here. See G. G. Simpson, "Evolutionary Determinism and the Fossil Record" (*Sci. Monthly*, 71 [1950], 262-267).

as we please is simply unrealistic in a material cosmos, but this is obviously no argument against the fact that we do have a measure of conscious control over what becomes of us.[7] The intelligent exploitation of this possibility depends, of course, not only on determination of its means but also on recognition of its limits. Some attempt to consider the future possibilities will be made in the last chapter.

In preceding pages evidence was given, thoroughly conclusive evidence, as I believe, that organic evolution is a process entirely materialistic in its origin and operation, although no explicit conclusion was made or considered possible as to the origin of the laws and properties of matter in general under which organic evolution operates. Life is materialistic in nature, but it has properties unique to itself which reside in its organization, not in its materials or mechanics. Man arose as a result of the operation of organic evolution and his being and activities are also materialistic, but the human species has properties unique to itself among all forms of life, superadded to the properties unique to life among all forms of matter and of action. Man's intellectual, social, and spiritual natures are altogether exceptional among animals in degree, but they arose by organic evolution. They usher in a new phase of evolution, and not a new phase merely but also a new kind, which is thus also a product of organic evolution and can be no less materialistic in its essence even though its organization and activities are essentially different from those in the process that brought it into being.

It has also been shown that purpose and plan are not characteristic of organic evolution and are not a key to any of its operations. But purpose and plan are characteristic in the new evolution, because man has purposes and he makes plans. Here purpose and plan do definitely enter into evolution, as a result and not as a cause of the processes seen in the long history of life. The purposes and plans are ours, not those of the universe, which displays convincing evidence of their absence.

Man was certainly not the goal of evolution, which evidently had no goal. He was not planned, in an operation wholly planless. He is not the ultimate in a single constant trend toward higher things, in a history of life with innumerable trends, none of them constant, and some toward the

[7] Yet there seems at the moment to be a minor vogue for the idea that because we do not control social evolution completely and with no limitation as to possibilities, we therefore do not control it at all! There is perhaps here too a touch of the false analogy between the two evolutions and a feeling that because organic evolution happens, willy-nilly, to, say, sparrows, this is true also of social evolution and man. For an able (yet, I cannot but conclude, essentially fallacious) exposition of this point of view, see L. A. White, "Man's Control over Civilization: an Anthropocentric Illusion" (*Sci. Monthly*, 66 [1948], 235-247).

lower rather than the higher. Is his place in nature, then, that of a mere accident, without significance? The affirmative answer that some have felt constrained to give is another example of the "nothing but" fallacy. The situation is as badly misrepresented and the lesson as poorly learned when man is considered nothing but an accident as when he is considered as the destined crown of creation. His rise was neither insignificant nor inevitable. Man *did* originate after a tremendously long sequence of events in which both chance and orientation played a part. Not all the chance favored his appearance, none *might* have, but enough did. Not all the orientation was in his direction, it did not lead unerringly humanward, but some of it came this way. The result *is* the most highly endowed organization of matter that has yet appeared on the earth—and we certainly have no good reason to believe there is any higher in the universe. To think that this result is insignificant would be unworthy of that high endowment, which includes among its riches a sense of values.

10. The Search for an Ethic

MAN IS a moral animal. With the exception of a few peculiar beings who are felt to be as surely crippled as if the deformity were physical, all men make judgments of good or bad in ethics and morals. All feel some degree of compulsion to value and promote the good, to condemn and eliminate the bad. It requires no demonstration that a demand for ethical standards is deeply ingrained in human psychology. Like so many human characteristics, indeed most of them, this trait is both innate and learned. Its basic mechanism is evidently part of our biological inheritance. The degree of development of this, in the individual and in society, as well as the particular form that it will take are conditioned by learning processes in the family and in the wider aspects of the social structure. Man almost inevitably acquires an ethic and this responds to a deep need in any normal member of the species. The reasons for this need and the immediate elements in its fulfillment are among the most important of subjects for the study of man, but they are, on the whole, outside our present enquiry. It suffices here to recognize the fact that the need does exist.[1]

[1] In the volume by the two Huxleys previously cited, Julian Huxley has devoted special attention to the origin and development of the individual moral sense, basing himself mainly on Freudian theory.

Through the ages ethical standards responding to this need have been supplied mainly from three closely interrelated sources: introspection, authority, and convention. The basis of acceptance has been intuitive, the feeling of rightness, without objective enquiry into the reasons for this feeling and without possible test as to the truth or falseness of the premises involved. Introspection may produce results so intensely felt and within such an emotional framework that they are considered as having sanction and force from some external, nonmaterial source, that is, they are taken to be inspired and divine in origin. They then become revelations. Such introspective revelations of a gifted few may in time be accepted by many others as valid, just as may also the introspections of philosophers who do not claim to have received revelations. The ethic is then bolstered by authority, the authority of the individual philosopher or of the presumed Inspirer. Second-hand acceptance of revelation or of philosophical introspection is usually as intuitive as were the original introspections. The acceptability of an ethical system has generally corresponded with wishful thinking in the individual, who firmly believes what he enjoys believing, and with some sort of pragmatic validation in society. Conviction that the system is right is confirmed by the feeling that it works. The individual is comforted and made happier by a system that responds to his own wishes (so obscure in origin), and any particular society does operate better by erection of standards automatically, although seldom perfectly, adjusted to that society by the fact that they arise and evolve in it.

The mass of people usually find that their own introspective judgment of right and wrong, the edicts of the authorities accepted by them, and the conventions of their society coincide rather closely. They coincide because their sources are related and because the individuals in society tend to modify them or to ignore their discrepancies so as to produce the illusion, at least, of coincidence. The martyrs who cling to a supposedly revealed ethic that is not accepted by their society and the social rebels whose introspective standards reject convention are relatively few in number—although, of course, new systems which may later become conventional arise among such martyrs and rebels.

In all cases satisfaction with the accepted system of ethics, the feeling of a filled need and of emotional security, has depended in large measure on conviction that the system is absolute. It is believed to provide standards of right and wrong which are eternally and everywhere valid, for which the individual has no responsibility other than simple acceptance.

The basis for belief in the intuitive systems of ethics with their claims of eternal and ubiquitous validity was thoroughly shaken by the discovery that they are, in fact, highly relative. Their validation by intuition and their introspective origin itself were found by the psychologists, largely as a result of the Freudian revolution, to depend on learning and psychological conditioning, mainly in early childhood. They are entirely relative to these processes and their intuitive validation is apparent and equally strong in ethical systems diametrically opposite in tendency. The anthropologists found further that extremely diverse ethical systems exist in different societies, all equally valid as far as pragmatic or other objective tests go, and that they are decidedly relative to social structure and other factors that have nothing to do with their absolute validity.[2]

This demonstration that intuitive ethics are relative and cannot, by their very nature, provide an absolute ethical criterion spurred a search that had, indeed, become widespread even before the demonstration was complete. The attempt was to reach an ethic by a process as little intuitive as possible, to turn to nature, the material cosmos, and to try to deduce standards of conduct from its objective phenomena. The search for a naturalistic ethic was begun long before Darwin, but it was prematurely intensified in the latter part of the nineteenth century with recognition that evolution is a phenomenon of nature which must have ethical bearings. The intensification was premature because the evolutionary process was still insufficiently understood and its possible ethical significance similarly subject to misunderstanding.[3]

The search for a naturalistic ethical system has had as its basis confidence in observation and experiment as leading to discovery of objective truth, or increasing approximation to it, and the conviction that what is ethically right is related in some way to what is materially true. On the negative side, the premise is that there is no necessary relationship between the results of introspection alone and truth or right. These propositions are themselves subjective value judgments and their validity is open to discussion, which it has already received in large measure. A good case can be made out in detail for these convictions, but perhaps their best justification lies in the fact

---

[2] These facts were abundantly demonstrated in E. Westermarck's *Ethical Relativity* (London, Paul, Trench, Trubner, 1932).

[3] These earlier attempts to find a naturalistic ethic were reviewed rather thoroughly but with great hostility by W. F. Quillian, Jr., *The Moral Theory of Evolutionary Naturalism* (New Haven, Yale University Press, 1945). Although his work has value as a historical review, Quillian seems to have been wholly unaware of any recent developments in this field or of the fact that, when he wrote, there was hardly a single one of the students of evolution who held the views he ascribed to them. Julian Huxley has well reviewed and refuted Quillian's book in his introduction to *Touchstone for Ethics*, already cited.

that, even if they had to be taken as articles of faith, they would still be in large measure self-justifying in being fully consistent with our knowledge of nature and of man's place in nature. This seems to me to be sufficiently evident in preceding and following discussion and at this point I am inclined to abbreviate by simply postulating these principles not as ethics in themselves but as the basis on which a valid ethic must rest. Of course this does not involve endorsement of any particular ethical system erected ostensibly on the same basis, for it will quickly be seen that a majority of these will not stand up when judged on this very basis.

Many of Darwin's immediate followers thought of evolution primarily in terms of struggle, a concept consistent with and based on Darwinian selection, but not carried to such excess by Darwin himself. They evolved what T. H. Huxley called "the gladiatorial theory of existence" and concluded that the evolutionary ethic must be, first, every man for himself, then every tribe, every nation, every class, and so on, for itself in the "struggle for existence." Such tooth-and-claw ethics suited the book of Victorian laissez faire capitalism and also, with only rather superficial remodeling, of its opposing ideology in Marxist socialism. Those who were not suited by this wholly superficial interpretation of an ill-understood natural process found themselves in a serious dilemma. They could not believe that unbounded personal competition, exploitation and dominance of one group by another, class and national warfare, and the other concomitants of a gladiatorial existence were ethically right. But on the other hand they believed that these are the essential features of the evolutionary process. T. H. Huxley concluded that evolution, although it is a fact that must be faced, is ethically bad. Man's problem then becomes not the forwarding of the evolutionary process but its thwarting. Huxley accepted "the essential evil of the world" and only hoped it could be abated by ethical human conduct. He endorsed and accepted the intuitive ethics of his time as non-, in fact anti-, evolutionary and did not even discuss their origin or validity.[4]

The repercussions of this unreal dilemma and of the fallacious tooth-and-claw ethics are still sadly with us. Their influence has been unqualifiedly pernicious. The fact that this

[4] See his Romanes Lecture, reprinted by Julian Huxley in *Touchstone for Ethics.*

A similar idea has been developed at greater length by Sir Arthur Keith in an extraordinary book, *Evolution and Ethics* (New York, Putnam, 1946), whose recent date makes it a gross anachronism. Sir Arthur gives an extended and horrendous exposition of tooth-and-claw ethics, which he never quite condemns and which he thinks inherent in evolution. With this he contrasts human or (as he insists) anti-evolutionary ethics. In spite of talking all around every side of the problem, he never quite faces the issue as to which set of ethics can or should be followed or how they are to be reconciled.

widely hailed product of the search was certainly bad has cast a shadow over the whole effort to find a naturalistic ethic, and should certainly make us extremely cautious in our continuance of that search.

The tooth-and-claw ethic was based on the propositions that evolution as a whole has been ethically good and that its process is gladiatorial. T. H. Huxley saw no alternative to tooth-and-claw ethics except the opposite conclusion that evolution as a whole is ethically bad. The dilemma thus set up was unreal on both sides, for it was neither established that the tooth-and-claw ethic is inherent in evolution as a whole nor that what is inherent in evolution as a whole constitutes a fit guide for human life. Aside from details, very basic misapprehensions regarding evolution, as we now know it, were involved. Literal struggle is *not* the essence of natural selection, and natural selection itself is only one of many different factors in evolution. Attention was focused on speciation and the process of speciation was falsely viewed as a competitive struggle between groups of organisms. Furthermore other far more important aspects of evolution were wholly overlooked and the whole course of history viewed in terms of speciation only. There was no reason why speciation, even if it had been correctly understood, should have been taken as *the* basis for an evolutionary ethic. The tooth-and-claw ethic was thoroughly unjustified. Its excesses and its truly unethical conclusions do not follow from the principles of evolution, and this failure need not put an end to the search for an evolutionary ethic.

Herbert Spencer, still under the sway of the gladiatorial theory of evolution current in his day, was among the first to seek to avoid the ferocity of the conclusions that seemed to arise from this theory by proposing one of many varieties of what may be called "life ethics." The postulate is that life is good. Ethical conduct is that which promotes life. Evolution is good, on the whole, because it has promoted life, also on the whole. From determining how evolution has best accomplished this, we can draw guidance as to how we too can promote life. If our conduct does promote life, it will be ethical. Evolution is not over-all a safe guide, but must be viewed selectively. Extinction is a normal part of evolution, but it does not promote life and is therefore ethically wrong. These are some of the conclusions characteristic of the different sorts of life ethics, of which there are many variants now upheld by students of evolution.

Baldly put, the life ethic becomes simply a survival ethic: what best promotes survival is good, what endangers survival is bad. In logical extreme, this becomes only another variant of the old tooth-and-claw ethic. If individual survival is the ultimate good, then it is every man for himself again. (And incidentally, the man who dies for a cause is bad, whether the cause be bad or good; the father who endangers his own life in attempt to rescue his child is bad, and so on.) This extreme is avoided by making group or racial, not individual, survival the goal, but still the ethic is not satisfactory.[5] Of course survival is a condition for any progress or for any continuing medium in which good can exist, but what is basically good, in a moral sense, about survival in itself and what part of the evolutionary process could lead us to take this as an ethical guide? Survival is well assured, we have seen, by arrested evolution, by equilibrium in a static environment. Man himself, who needs the ethic, would never have arisen by such survival. Survival for a longer or shorter time is gained by the most diverse and contradictory means, by progression and by retrogression, by specialization and by adaptability, by parasitism—by such a variety of means that to call them all "good" becomes meaningless and certainly offers no hope of an ethical standard for man. And do not forget that survival is ultimately impossible. All life will cease some day. We may and do hope, surely, that mankind will survive as long as possible, but survival will have no ethical significance except as man be good or bad by other standards than merely existing. Certainly it is "good" to survive, but we fall into a semantic trap if we think that this is an *ethical* good.

By a logical extension, the survival ethic becomes an ethic of satisfaction and harmony. It is "good" to survive, for the individual, for the species, and ultimately for all of life. As Leake has said in a development of this thesis, "Relationships between the individuals and groups in contact with each other to be 'good' must therefore be conducive toward the survival of all concerned." Then the general principle appears that "The probability of survival of individual, or groups of, living things increases with the degree with which they harmoniously adjust themselves to each other and their environment." [6] This is the very opposite of the tooth-and-claw ethic. It is based on a much truer conception of the evolutionary process and of the processes of life in general. It also has the virtue of being congruous with almost any ethic, except the plainly false tooth-and-claw ethic, that can be based on the evolutionary process. That is, almost any other naturalistic system

<hr />

[5] In spite of the serious weaknesses of Quillian's attack on naturalistic ethics, previously noted, he made a very telling point in emphasizing that this particular variety of evolutionary ethics is based on implicit belief in an unconditional obligation to survive, or to avoid extinction. The obligation is not demonstrated, nor is it clearly good or worthy.

[6] Both quotations are from the following thoughtful and valuable paper: C. D. Leake, "Ethicogenesis" (*Sci. Monthly, 60* [1945], 245-253).

of ethics would agree that behavior consistent with this principle would usually be ethical.

Action on this principle would usually tend to *promote* good, and yet it does not seem to be a basic criterion for judging what *is* good. It still departs from the postulate that survival is "good," and we have noted that this is not necessarily true in an ethical sense. Moreover, this is a purely static concept. It would seem logically to involve a changeless equilibrium, with maximum or complete harmony, as the highest good. If this implication is accepted, then the principle is unrealistic and is not evolutionary, nor surely good. The tooth-and-claw ethic is invalid, but there are teeth and claws in nature. Some organisms must die if others are to live. And evolution involves ceaseless change. Even extinction of races and of whole orders and classes has been a condition of the rise of higher types. The harmonious equilibrium is never reached, and if it had been, man would not now exist. The equilibrium is not achieved with the coming of man, nor is there apparent opportunity for him to attain it.

A further step in the search accepts and emphasizes the dynamic nature of life and of its evolution. Departing, still, from the proposition that life is good, the dynamic inference is that increase in life is good. Whatever tends to increase life is therefore right, and whatever tends to decrease it is wrong—an ethic of increase or of abundance of life. Here again, action under this principle would often or usually be ethical by most other standards of ethics, but reflection raises doubts as to whether the principle is itself ethical, that is, a standard by which right and wrong action may be judged. Its applicability is far narrower than that of the ethic of harmony, which does not contradict it. How many concrete situations can you think of in which you could decide on right and wrong action, as an individual or for a nation or for mankind as a whole, on the basis of consequent increase or decrease in life? Murder becomes bad, to be sure, but most situations which do have ethical bearings elude application of the principle. Other problems, where it does somehow bear, require some other and overriding principle for solution. It is good to plant a crop, but is it good or bad to harvest it? And is this situation, to which the principle definitely applies although the direction of the application is equivocal, really an ethical one at all? Evidently if the principle is ethical it is severely limited and inadequate as basis for a system of ethics.

Further thought must raise some doubt as to whether the principle would indeed lead to right and to the avoidance of wrong. Which is right and which wrong: an earth so crowded with men that they can barely subsist by laboring all their waking hours and any further increase is cut off by starvation, or an earth moderately populated and with ample provision for all? The alternatives now exist as between, say, parts of China or India and most of the United States. Trend toward maximum population and minimum subsistence is necessarily right and good under the increase ethic. Judgment that it is wrong and bad would be suspect if merely intuitive, but as will appear, this judgment does follow from an ethic more soundly based in the history of life than is the increase ethic.

Various forms of the ethic of increase of life are commonly derived from or supported by the statement that this constitutes a major trend of evolution. This ethic then becomes one of many, sometimes contradictory, possible and proposed ethical systems which depend on the postulate that continuation of the trend, or of a trend, in past evolution is an ethical guide to right conduct and to future good. Such a conclusion follows almost automatically from a finalist view of evolution, especially when this is put on a theistic or otherwise religious basis. If evolution has a goal, if it has all been a progression toward some ultimate and determining end, then we should find out that goal by observations of the facts of evolution and it is reasonable to consider further progress toward the goal as ethically right. This becomes not only reasonable but also obligatory if the goal was set by God. Unfortunately for hopes for so simple a solution of the ethical problem, the basis for this is flatly nonexistent. There is no real evidence whatever that evolution has had a goal, and there is overwhelming evidence that it has not.

Evolution does have trends, many of them, and it has been seen that the most nearly general of these has been toward increase in the total of life on the earth. Hence the increase ethic would seem to be validated if trend ethics were acceptable as valid. But all trend ethics demand the postulate that the trends of evolution or some particular one among these is ethically right and good. There is no evident reason why such a postulate should be accepted. It is, at least, impossible to conclude that *all* evolutionary trends are ipso facto good. They are too diverse and they lead as often to decrease of life and to ultimate extinction as to increase and survival. The problem arises that a choice must be made; it is necessary to decide *which* trends are good. The decision cannot, then, be based on factual observation that a trend has occurred but must involve some other and quite distinct ethical criterion. Any attempt to find a valid trend ethic results merely in a requirement that some other ethic first be found in order to select the right ethical trend. Thus the increase ethic is not validated because it follows a general trend in evolution, but on the contrary, identification of that trend as right depends on prior admission of the validity of the increase ethic—an admission which, as previously shown, is neither forced nor warranted by what is known of the evolutionary process.

There is another group of attempts to derive ethics from aspects of the evolutionary history of life which is often, but not necessarily, supported by the fallacious argument from trend. These proposed systems, which might collectively be called aggregation ethics, see as ethically good the increased aggregation of organic units into higher levels of organization. One form of the argument runs more or less as follows: Evolution has involved a succession of organic levels, with progressive complication and perfection of coordinated structure and function on each level. The protozoans and other one-celled (or noncellular, or cellularly undivided) organisms represent a lowest level. The next level is that of multicellular individuals, metazoans, with increasing differentiation of the cells and their grouping into organs with increasingly specialized functions. There follows another level, the highest, in which metazoan individuals are aggregated into hyperzoan organisms. The hyperzoan or "epi-organism" is society, into which individuals are to merge and be integrated as subordinate parts of a higher whole. It is, in fact, the so-called organic state, considered as having an individuality and life of its own. In such a state individuals, or "persons," as some adherents of this view prefer to call them, exist for the state, the good and rights of which are separate from and superior to that of the individuals composing it.[7]

The whole argument and its ethical implications, among which may be support of authoritarian and totalitarian ideologies as biologically and ethically right, are thoroughly erroneous. When the state or any other social structure is called an "organism," the word is being used in a way fundamentally different from its use for a biological organism such as an ameba, a tree, or you. The state is not an individual or a person in anything like the same sense that these organisms are individuals. The parts that compose it retain, and indeed intensify, their organic individuality. Their relationship to the social unit is entirely different from the relationship of cells or

[7] The organismic theory of the state was pre-evolutionary and in its modern form seems to stem directly from Comte. It was left for some modern biologists to "discover," wholly falsely, as I believe, that the trend of evolution confirms the organic nature of the state, makes this biologically "right," and establishes as the basis for ethics the promotion of the state as an organism. Among those who have most insistently and fully expressed this idea is the physiologist R. W. Gerard, for instance in "A Biological Basis for Ethics" (*Philosophy of Science, 9* [1942], 92-120). The whole complicated subject of organic levels was rather fully treated from many points of view, including that of Gerard and the "epi-organism school," in R. Redfield, *Levels of Integration in Biological and Social Systems* (Lancaster, Pennsylvania, Jaques Cattell, 1942).

organs to a metazoan individual. Calling a state an "organism" and concluding that it is therefore comparable with a metazoan organism is a glaring example of the fallacy of the shifting middle term. Use of the comparison as an analogy provides an interesting descriptive metaphor, but its use in support of an aggregation ethic is a particularly egregious misuse of analogy, confusing it with equivalence and extending it as an interpretive principle far beyond the point to which it is valid even as metaphorical description.

Furthermore, if the fallacious use of "organism" as a shifting term is avoided, it is quite evident that merging of the individual into a higher organic unit is not a common trend in evolution and, specifically, is not at all a trend in human evolution. The trend in human evolution and in many other evolutionary sequences has been, on the contrary, toward greater individualization. The particular type of social organization characteristic of man, as opposed, say, to that in an anthill, has been based on high individualization of its members and has intensified this. It will be necessary to refer again to this fact, and to clarify some of its implications, in the next chapter in connection with what I believe to be a truer conception of the ethical significance of man's place in nature and of his evolution.

These various attempts to find a naturalistic ethic where it is most likely to reside, in the process of evolution, have certainly greatly clarified the issues involved. They have narrowed the field of search and most of them have, at worst, skirted an acceptable solution. At best they have produced partial answers which are indeed ethically good although not achieving a general and firmly based evolutionary ethic. It is now clear that none of the attempts reviewed up to this point can be considered satisfactory. All were seeking a more coherent and realistic basis for ethics than could be found in the older intuitive systems, and in this we must conclude that they were on the right track, but in so doing they have not escaped all the pitfalls of those older systems.

Most of these naturalistic ethics have been attempts, as were intuitive ethics, to find standards of right and wrong with eternal validity for all things from ameba to man. This adherence to an ideal absolutism fails in appreciation of two basic facts of evolution: that change is of its essence and that man represents a new, unique sort of organism subject to a new, distinct sort of evolution in addition to the older sort, which still continues. The need and the search for an ethic are also unique to man and in fact ethics enters into evolution only at this point; ethical judgment arises in the new evolution and is one of its characteristics. There are no ethics but human ethics, and a search that ignores the necessity that ethics be human, relative to man, is bound to fail. Attempts to derive an ethic from evolution as a whole, without particular reference to man, are further examples of the "nothing but" fallacy of the nature of man.

Another basic weakness in not quite all but most of these attempts has been that they involve trying to find out what evolution has been up to, or even what evolution seems to *want,* and then assuming that promotion of this is ethically right. This amounts to placing evolution in the position occupied by God or by His revelation in intuitive ethics. Such naturalistic ethics share with those they attempted to replace a certain evasion of responsibility. They still try to find an external standard, one given without need for choice and without other requirements than discovery and acceptance.

So the enquiry seems to have swung in a circle and to be back rather near where it started. Yet there is a point from which to go on, and the unsatisfactory nature of these attempts does not preclude the possibility of others that can be satisfactory. The point is that an evolutionary ethic *for man* (which is of course the one we, as men, seek, if not the only possible kind) should be based on man's own nature, on his evolutionary position and significance. It cannot be expected to arise *automatically* from the principles of evolution in general, nor yet, indeed, from those of human evolution in particular. It cannot be expected to be absolute, but must be subject to evolution itself and must be the result of responsible and rational *choice* in the full light of such knowledge of man and of life as we have.

11. *The Ethics of Knowledge and of Responsibility*

THE MEANING that we are seeking in evolution is its meaning to us, to man. The ethics of evolution must be human ethics. It is one of the many unique qualities of man, the new sort of animal, that he is the only ethical animal. The ethical need and its fulfillment are also products of evolution, but they have been produced in man alone.

Man's knowledge that he exists is, at the least, more conscious and particular than that of any other animal. Man alone knows that he has evolved and is still doing so. Man alone places himself in a conceptual framework of space and time. Man possesses purpose and exercises deliberate choice to a unique degree, even if, indeed, these capacities can be said to be the same in kind in any other animals. It is most improbable that any other animal has more than an inchoate or largely instinctual sense of values, while in man this is normally conscious, orderly, and controlled. (This does not contradict the fact that, even in man, the *origin* of his valuations is in considerable part unconscious and may be quite uncontrolled.)

Conscious knowledge, purpose, choice, and values carry as an inevitable corollary responsibility. Capacity for knowledge involves responsibility for finding out the truth and, in our social system, for communicating this. The possibility of choice brings an ethical responsibility for selection of what is right. The sense of values implies means and responsibility for decision as to what is right. Purpose confers the power and, again, the responsibility for translating choice and value into right action. These capacities and responsibilities are not qualities of life in general or of its evolution, but specifically of man. Man is much the most knowing or thinking animal, as our predecessors rightly recognized in bestowing on him the distinctive qualification of *sapiens*. Man is also the responsible animal. This is more basic than his knowledge, although dependent on it, for some other animals surely know and think in a way not completely inhuman, but no other animal can truly be said to be responsible in anything like the same sense in which man is responsible.

The search for an absolute ethic, either intuitive or naturalistic, has been a failure. Survival, harmony, increase of life, integration of organic or social aggregations, or other such suggested ethical standards are characteristics which may be present in varying degrees, or absent, in organic evolution but they are not really ethical principles independent and absolute. They become ethical principles only if man chooses to make them such. Man cannot evade the responsibility of the choice. As his knowledge embraces facts about these characteristics in evolution, they become part of the basis on which his ethical principles should be developed, but they supply no automatic guide to good and bad.

Man has risen, not fallen. He can choose to develop his capacities as the highest animal and to try to rise still farther, or he can choose otherwise. The choice is his responsibility, and his alone. There is no automatism that will carry him upward without choice or effort and there is no trend solely in the right direction. Evolution has no purpose; man must supply this for himself. The means to gaining right ends involve both organic evolution and human evolution, but human choice as to what *are* the right ends must be based on human evolution. It is futile to search for an absolute ethical criterion retroactively in what occurred before ethics themselves evolved. The best human ethical standard must be relative and particular to man and is to be sought rather in the new evolution, peculiar to man, than in the old, universal to all organisms. The old evolution was and is essentially amoral. The new evolution involves knowledge, including the knowledge of good and evil.

The most essential material factor in the new evolution seems to be just this: knowledge, together, necessarily, with its spread and inheritance. As a first proposition of evolutionary ethics derived from specifically human evolution, it is submitted that promotion of knowledge is essentially good. This is a basic material ethic. "Promotion" involves both the acquisition of new truths or of closer approximations to truth (metaphorically the mutations of the new evolution) and also its spread by communication to others and by their acceptance and learning of it (metaphorically its heredity). This ethic of knowledge is not complete and independent. In itself knowledge is necessarily good, but it is effective only to the degree that it does spread in a population, and its results may then be turned by human choice and responsible action for either good or evil.

These considerations suggest some notice of the mechanisms for acquiring knowledge, of values in knowledge, and of its right and wrong utilization—subjects obviously too vast for adequate discussion here and yet too important to be passed over in total silence. Knowledge is of many sorts and is to be sought in no one way. Perception of tenderness and of security acquired at the mother's breast is as truly knowledge as is determination of the fabric of an alloy acquired at the electron microscope. Science is, however, our most successful and systematic means of acquiring knowledge and, at present, almost alone in the power to acquire knowledge wholly new to man. It used to be usual to claim that value judgments have no part in science, but we are coming more and more to perceive how false this was. Science is essentially interwoven with such judgments. The very existence of science demands the value judgment and essential ethic that knowledge is good. The additional and still more fundamental ethic of responsibility makes scientists individually responsible for evaluating the knowledge that they acquire, for transmitting it as may be right, and for its ultimate utilization for good.

A broad classification of the sciences into physical, biological, and social corresponds with three levels of organization of matter and energy, and not levels only, but also quite distinct kinds of organization. The three are of sharply increasing orders of complexity and each includes the lower grades. Vital organization is more intricate than physical organization and it is added to and does not replace physical organization, which is also fully involved in vital organization. Social organization retains and sums the complexities of both of these and adds its own still greater complexities.

Many of the dangers and ethical problems of science arise from these relationships. At one end, the universal basis of scientific knowledge is in the physical sciences, and they can produce most far-reaching results, for good or evil. The physical sciences are much the simplest of the three groups. Discoveries here are made more readily and more rapidly, so that advances of knowledge in this field are accelerated. But the physical sciences, which for these reasons need for their guidance the most rigid and continuous application of ethical standards, are farthest removed from the source of those standards and the means of their application. At the other end, this source and these means lie in the social sciences, but they are by far the most difficult and intricate. Their discoveries demand much more travail and are slower to be reached, far slower to be disseminated and utilized. Their ethical guidance is no less important than that of the physical sciences, but they have the added complication that they are themselves the lumber room of ethics, crowded with old, conflicting, and certainly partly false ethical systems and the battleground of these. To mention only one dilemma arising from this situation, the physical sciences have put man in possession of the awful secret of atomic energy before the social sciences have produced any means of controlling this or of securing its ethical application. The inequity of knowledge is in itself unethical and is one of man's great blunders. It could be his last.

The possibilities of wrong in the unequal development or in the results of the spread of knowledge reveal the need for another ethic, one that may be more profound or, at least, that shall have a moral rather than a mainly material basis. A second essential feature arising from the unique status of man in the history of life was seen to be his possession of personal responsibility. It is now submitted that the highest and most essential moral ethical standards are involved in the fact of man's personal responsibility.

This responsibility is not in itself an ethic. It is a fact, a fundamental and peculiar characteristic of the human species established by his evolution and evident in his relationship to the rest of the cosmos. Recognition of this responsibility and its proper exercise are the firm basis on which right and moral human action must be based. From it arises a pervasive ethic which, among other things, may ensure the right interpretation and action of the ethic of knowledge. Human responsibility requires, in each individual as well as in society as a whole, that the search for knowledge be a search for truth, as unbiased as is possible to human beings; that probable truths as discovered be tested by every means that can be devised, that these truths be communicated in such a way as is most likely to ensure their right utilization and incorporation into the general body of human knowledge, and that those who should receive this knowledge seek it, share in its communication, and in their turn examine and test with as little prejudice as possible whatever is submitted as truth. This is a large order, indeed, but a necessary one. It involves responsibilities for every living person, and responsibilities that cannot be ethically evaded; that is, their evasion is morally wrong. Among other consequences of this morality, it follows that blind faith (simple acceptance without review of evidence or rational choice between alternatives) is immoral. Such faith is immoral whether it is placed in a theological doctrine, a political platform, or a scientific theory.

Of course this does not mean that every individual must become a theologian before it is moral for him to join a church, a political economist before it is moral to vote, or a research biologist before it is moral to accept the truth of evolution. The field of knowledge is obviously far too vast, and human mentality far too limited, for each of us to grasp all these intricacies. It is a social requirement that there be specialists in each field whose profession it is to examine and to test such truths as pertain to it. It is the moral duty of these specialists to submit their qualifications, the results of their judgment, and such general evidence for it as is essential for its substantiation. When such judgments conflict, as they often do on a given point, the moral duty of the non-specialist is to choose the judgments of that authority whose qualifications are greatest in the pertinent field and whose submitted evidence is best. The individual remains personally responsible for making the choice, even if he must do so on the basis of the knowledge of others and not his personal knowledge.

Neither this nor any other process can rigidly guarantee making the right choice. It is not to be taken as an appeal to authority in the sense of belief in the absolute validity of any one opinion or of infallibility in science or in religion. The important point is responsibility for using the right *method* of choice. The right method is evaluation of evidence and avoidance of pure intuition and of authoritarian dogma. Recourse to authority, in this context, demands judgment that the accepted opinion is based on rational consideration of known evidence. It is the rejection of revelation or of emotional reaction when knowledge is available. It further rejects the absolute nature of any authority. Choice must be prepared to change if increase in knowledge or its better interpretation occurs.

Beyond its relationship to the ethic of knowledge, the fact of responsibility has still broader ethical bearings. The responsibility is basically personal and becomes social only as it is extended in society among the individuals composing the social unit. It is correlated with another human evolutionary characteristic, that of high individualization. From this relationship arises the ethical judgment that it is good, right, and moral to recognize the integrity and dignity of the individual and to promote the realization or fulfillment of individual capacities. It is bad, wrong, and immoral to fail in such recognition or to impede such fulfillment. This ethic applies first of all to the individual himself and to the integration and development of his own personality. It extends farther to his social group and to all mankind. Negatively, it is wrong to develop one individual at the expense of any other. Positively, it is right to develop all in the greatest degree possible to each within the group as a whole. Individuals vary greatly in other capacities, but integrity and dignity are capable of equal development in all.

Socialization and individualization may conflict, but they may also work together for the advancement of each. Here again choice is possible, and not only a possibility but also an unavoidable responsibility. Individual integration and welfare can be secured at the expense of others, but they may also be achieved, and reach their highest degree, by interaction which promotes others along with the self. Under this system of ethical standards a definition of the good society might indeed be simply that it is a society in which this interaction is usual.

An individual in society leads no existence wholly apart from that society, any more than the most solitary individual of any species of organisms can exist without reference to its environment. The social group is part of the human environment, a largely self-constructed part. It is the medium in which the individual exists and it is one of the molding, evolutionary influences on the individual. The abstraction of a human individual not so molded and influenced is completely unreal.[1] Flexibility in reaction to the environment, especially including the social environment, is a major characteristic of the human species and is the essence of human individualization. A human organism that developed outside of such a framework, if this were possible, would certainly be far less individualized than one developed within it. Human personality and accompanying individualization, with all its amazing variety, depend on interaction with the environment to a far greater degree than does the lesser individualization of any other organisms. The sorts of human society that we call civilized all demand and are based on a rather high minimum of variability and of individualization in its members, a minimum far above that reached by any nonhuman species. In turn, such a society provides the possibility of degrees of individualization far greater than could ever be achieved outside it. In biological terms, it provides a variety of ecological niches much greater than those of primitive tribal society and tremendously greater than those available to any other species of organisms. The niches are filled by individual adjustability to larger extent than by genetic adjustment.[2]

The apparent conflict of socialization and individualization thus does not really exist, and suggestion of choice between one or the other presents unreal alternatives. Individualization is a means of socialization and socialization provides enriched opportunities for individualization.[3]

[1] In a recent conference, mainly of anthropologists, on socialization and evolution there was some, although not unanimous, agreement that the word "individual" implied such an abstraction and that the social individual should be called a "person." This seems to me poor semantics and absurd biology. The biological individual (one is hardly going to call an ant or a crow a "person"!) is precisely the nonabstract, concrete organic unit which obviously and inevitably exists within and as a part of a total environmental situation. The species, or other taxonomic unit, is the biological abstraction; this has no individuality or *personality*, although even it cannot be considered as existing merely in a vacuum. The concept of a human "person" who is not an "individual," who does not possess individuality but is only a nondescript unit in a social group, is a complete abstraction in social science. Substitution of "person" for "individual" is certainly not a step in the direction of concreteness or reality, or of a workable system of ethics.

[2] The plasticity of man and his great capacity for personal adaptation are briefly and well discussed by Th. Dobzhansky and M. F. Ashley Montagu in "Natural Selection and the Mental Capacities of Mankind" (*Science, 105* [1947], 587-590).

[3] A distinct but parallel, equally unreal dichotomy is sometimes presented in the study of organic, rather than social, evolution. Interbreeding populations evolve; individuals do the breeding, the being born, the living, and the dying that produce that evolution. The false alternatives are involved in the query whether it is the population or individuals that determine the process. In view of the facts of the process, these alternatives simply do not exist and the question is essentially meaningless.

Some years ago, as World War II was plainly approaching us, I presented a discussion of this general topic in "The Role of the Individual in Evolution" (*Jour. Washington Acad. Sciences, 31* [1941], 1-20). The presentation was frankly one sided because I was trying to make one point as strongly as possible, the point that the organismic theory of society is invalid and that biology and evolution do not support totalitarian ideology, as some of my colleagues had suggested. Invoking false alternatives in their fields, some students of organic evolution thought that my discussion of the individual's role in evolution involved rejection of the role of populations, and some students of social evolution thought that socialization was being opposed in favor of "rugged individualism" or laissez faire capitalism. I mention this now to preclude repetition of the same misunderstanding and also to refer the reader to this earlier and more one-sided but still I think generally consistent and valid discussion of one particular aspect of the present subject.

Another equally false set of alternatives is presented by any contrasting of collective action or security with personal responsibility. The collective aspects of the state are, or ethically should be, achieved by means of personal responsibility in all its members. Collective social measures, including provision for the underprivileged, are, or ethically should be, undertaken to prevent unethical development of some individuals at the expense of others and to promote the ethical equal development of all to the extent of their capacities. Such measures should not, and in the nature of things cannot, replace or eliminate personal responsibility but on the contrary require this and guarantee it, if they are both ethical and effective.

Collective action to promote individual development and to prevent exploitation is evidently required by an ethically good society, but its results can also be ethically bad. It can reinforce but can also contravene the ethical principles of personal responsibility and of individual integrity and dignity. This inevitably results if the members of society feel that their responsibility is delegated in the collective action and ceases to be individual. The individual who needs protection and help is not relieved of his responsibility for himself by the existence of a social mechanism for his assistance. Under our ethic, it is equally wrong for the individual to fail to seek such help as he needs and for him to demand or even to accept such help as a replacement for self-responsibility. On the other side, the social provision under this ethic must, if it is to be ethically right, be only the required means by which each individual carries out his personal responsibility toward any other individual who needs protection or aid. The responsibility is not diminished and it remains in the individual; it is not transferred to the mechanism that implements it.

It is fundamental in all this that responsibility is rooted in the true nature of man. It has arisen from and is inherent in his evolutionary history and status. Responsibility is something that he has just because he is human, and not something that he can choose to accept or to refuse. It cannot be rejected or unconditionally handed over to others. The attempt to do this is ethically wrong, and the responsibility remains where it was. The delegation of responsibility, to the extent that this is possible and proper, involves continuing responsibility for the actions of the delegate. In the last analysis, personal responsibility is nondelegable. Not only is every individual personally responsible for any actions by delegates or representatives of his, but he cannot ethically, even in semblance, delegate any responsibility for his own actions and for all their results.

The sweeping and impersonal nature of these generalizations may suggest difficulties and exceptions when particular and personal situations are considered. Is, for instance, the individual or society responsible if a jobless workman steals to feed his starving family? On reflection, this will be seen to be another false alternative. Everyone involved is necessarily responsible. The workman is certainly responsible for his action. On the stated facts alone the action itself may be ethically either good or bad. It is good if there was no alternative involving a lesser total of injury and indignity, determined by striking a balance between the good done for the family and the harm done morally to the workman himself and materially to his victim and to others who might otherwise have obtained the stolen food or who must indirectly pay for it. It is bad if avoidable harm is done, if, for instance, the workman has merely evaded responsibility for obtaining help in the social services available or for helping himself in a more proper way, such as accepting or seeking work. And in any case all other individuals in his society have a responsibility, which they may or may not have lived up to in the given case, first to see that sufficiently compensated work is available to the workman and second, in case of unavoidable failure in this, to see that the family is helped when help is needed beyond their own capacities.

As one more example, there is the old ethical problem of responsibility when an army officer orders a private to kill another human being. The situation is inherently bad: destruction of an individual is necessarily unethical on our premises. In a truly good society there would be no officer and no private. Pending the arrival of a good society, it is possible for such evil to be overbalanced by good resulting from the action. Whether the action was, in fact, more conducive to evil or to good in the particular circumstances, the officer and the private both have complete personal responsibility for it. The officer could not delegate the responsibility by giving an order and is as responsibile as if the shot were fired by his own hand. The private who does fire the shot cannot turn responsibility for his personal action back on the person or the circumstances inducing him to take the action. He has acquiesced in a situation where he knows that he is bound to carry out the orders of others. It was right for him to do so if in his judgment the ultimate result would be better than the result of his refusal to acquiesce. He remains responsible not only for this decision but also for any immediate actions, good or bad, that result from his being under orders.

Ethical standards based on the fundamental evolutionary characteristics of man, particularly on human knowledge and human responsibility, have the widest applications to human conduct and respond fully to the human need for judgment of right and wrong. The broadest problem now facing mankind is choice between conflicting ideologies. These evolutionary ethics here lead to unequivocal decisions.

Authoritarianism is wrong. The assignment of authority on a fixed basis, without constant check and periodic review, inevitably involves an attempt to delegate nondelegable responsibility and to evade responsibility for subsequent actions of the delegate. This is an ethically wrong denial of the personal responsibility inherent in man's nature. The system inevitably leads to exploitation of all by the authoritarian leader and the development of a hierarchy in which each higher group exploits those below it. This is a morally wrong development of some individuals not along with but at the expense of others.

Totalitarianism is wrong. The concept of a state as a separate entity with its own rights and responsibilities contravenes the biological and social fact that all rights and responsibilities are vested by nature in the individuals that compose the state. The claim that the welfare of the state is superior to that of any or all its component individuals is thus absurd on the face of it, and the claim inevitably is used to excuse denial of maximum opportunities for individual development by all, a denial which is immoral. Concomitants sure to occur in such a state are regimentation of individuals, policing of all conduct (including conduct ethically good), judgment of knowledge and of ideas on a basis other than that of their truth and falsity, and consequent suppression of truth and unethical control of the dissemination of knowledge. Totalitarianism cannot conceivably be reconciled with any ethical system that admits the goodness of knowledge, the ineradicable existence of personal responsibility, and the value of individual integrity and dignity.

Democracy is wrong in many of its current aspects and under some current definitions, but democracy is the only political ideology which can be made to embrace an ethically good society by the standards of ethics here maintained. Laissez faire capitalism, or any other societal activity that promotes or permits selfish or unfair utilization of some individuals by others, is obviously wrong by these standards. Capitalism, not further restricted, is perfectly consistent with authoritarianism or totalitarianism and is of course wrong if involved in either of those morally wrong systems. In a socialized democracy, controlled capitalism without improper exploitation may be ethically good. Majority rule is wrong if it involves suppression or oppression of any minority, but decision of problems by the majority of all those affected by them, accompanied by free expression of all opinions and full preserval of minority rights is, so far as has yet been demonstrated, the only possible ethically good means of reaching collective action. Attempts to assign personal responsibility to the government are ethically wrong (and biologically futile, to boot), but government by representatives or delegates for whose actions each one of their constituents remains personally responsible seems to be the only practicable method of ethical government for large groups of people.

Governments called democracies are by no means all ethically right by our standards, and none is free of many ethically bad aspects. Yet an ethically good state, one based on the fact of personal responsibility by each of its members and organized to promote the acquisition, dissemination, and acceptance of truth in all fields, to maintain the integrity and dignity of every individual, and to enable maximum possible realization of personal capacities—such a government would necessarily be a democracy.

Below these broadest aspects of the ethical problems of our times, application of these evolutionary ethics to personal problems and actions may be complex but is usually pertinent and decisive. A basic problem for all of us is the integration and ethical development of our own personalities. A major factor in this is certainly the acceptance and exercise of our personal responsibility. There is often no essential clinical difference in neurotic trends and strains or underlying personality factors between those who are socially normal, workably adjusted and integrated and those who are pathologically maladjusted.[4] The difference is essentially that the former have the ethically good will toward integration and take the responsibility for achievement of this in themselves. It follows, of course, that the maladjusted are in such cases (which admit of certain exceptions, as in the case of some traumatic psychoses) responsible for their own condition. The responsibility extends to the necessity for seeking help, from psychiatrists or others, when personal resources are not wholly sufficient, and it is a responsibility of every other member of society to see that such help is available and sufficient for those who do seek it.

It is, indeed, another inescapable biological fact that no

[4] It is important to insist on this point. It refutes with sufficient evidence from psychology itself an erroneous impression that post-Freudian views on the development of personality and of ethical mechanisms necessarily dilute or eliminate self-responsibility. See A. Roe, "The Use of Clinical Diagnostic Techniques in Research with Normals," pp. 336-342 of the symposium *Feelings and Emotions* (McGraw-Hill, 1950) and C. R. Rogers, *Client-centered Therapy* (Houghton Mifflin, 1951).

individual is fully self-sufficient, and the doctrine of personal responsibility carries no such illogical corollary. It is a responsibility not only with relationship to the self but also with relationship to others, ultimately embracing all of mankind, a responsibility for cooperation and for both giving and obtaining aid. This aspect of evolutionary ethics, above all others, begins in the cradle and follows us to the grave. Normal development of the human infant requires the presence of a mother and frequent contact with her.[5] Her responsibility in this matter is another that cannot be delegated. Withholding of continual affectionate contact or unnecessary assignment of care to an impersonal agency is immoral because it impedes normal integration of the infant's individuality.

In such a situation, and in many others, the bearing of these ethics is perfectly clear. They provide, however, no guide by which every action of daily life need be judged and channeled into a single possible direction. In most respects wide latitude remains between "right" and "wrong." It is, in fact, a part of the sense of values arising from these considerations that diversity in personality and in action is a good and positively valuable characteristic of mankind, so long as it does not overstep broad ethical bounds or impinge unfavorably on other personalities. Regimentation of personality or suppression of individuality is ethically bad by these standards. Respect for others is ethically good. Appreciation rather than bigoted disapproval of differences from ourselves is one of the means of enriching our own experiences and personalities, and this too is one of the ethical goods.

It should, finally, again be emphasized that these ethical standards are relative, not absolute. They are relative to man as he now exists on the earth. They are based on man's place in nature, his evolution, and the evolution of life, but they do not arise automatically from these facts or stand as an inevitable and eternal guide for human—or any other—existence. Part of their basis is man's power of choice and they, too, are subject to choice, to selection or rejection in accordance with their own principles. They are also subject to future change as man evolves; after all, if mankind does pursue the ethic of knowledge it should be able progressively to improve and refine any ethical system based on knowledge.

There is no ethical absolute that does not arise from error and illusion. These relativistic ethics have, at least, the merit of being honestly derived from what seems to be demonstrably true and clear.

[5] "Mother" in this sense cannot always be the biological mother and the process may be sufficiently normal with a mother substitute. It is, however, better for the mother to be the biological mother. The infant does not know the difference, but the mother herself does and this affects the psychological situation.

12. The Future of Man and of Life

EVOLUTION is clearly going on around us today. There is no obvious reason for its not continuing for many millions of years to come, as regards both man and the rest of the organic realm. It would be futile, in the present state of knowledge, to try to predict just what this future evolution will produce. It is, however, an essential part of study of the meaning of evolution to try to assess its present status and, not the future course, but the possibilities for the future inherent in the present condition of man and of other forms of life. Such assessment, made periodically as our knowledge increases, is also a necessary basis if we are eventually to make use of the unique human power to exercise a measure of control over evolution.

Some authorities[1] do, indeed, maintain that evolution is through, that life has evolved as far as possible and all essential evolutionary change stops at this point. A finalist could perhaps believe that evolution had a single aim, such as the production of man, and that it has stopped with achievement of that aim. But evolution is not, in fact, finalistic and it seems to me quite impossible for it to come to a standstill as long as there are any living organisms left to evolve. Life and its environment are in such ceaseless flux that it is simply inconceivable that a permanent equilibrium will ever be reached. Inability to predict just what evolution will do next is a sign of our ignorance, not of the impotence of evolution to do something more.

If an intelligent being had been able to study the world of, say, the Jurassic or Cretaceous without knowledge of what was to follow, he would have had as much reason as we have now to think that evolution had exhausted all possibilities. The world of life must then have seemed full to overflowing, with no opportunities overlooked. In reality, we know that extensive replacement has occurred in the ways of life then already occupied, and that new ways have in fact also been developed. It must also have seemed then that all existing

[1] Notably R. Broom, for instance, in "Evolution as the Palaeontologist Sees It" (*South African Jour. Sci.*, 29 [1933], 54-71). Broom has often returned to this point in later discussions of his extraordinary finalistic and metaphysical theory of evolution. Although I know of no other student who takes Broom's general theory seriously, a number of other students of evolution agree with him on this particular point, among them Julian Huxley, who, however, makes an exception for man. He has expressed the opinion that future evolution will occur *only* in man.

organisms were too specialized to give rise to any important new radiation. The few small and obscure mammals would have appeared to be merely highly and peculiarly specialized reptiles. It would seem extremely rash to predict that no form of life now in existence can possibly have similar potentialities for radiation on a new and unforeseen basis.

It has been suggested that *all* animals are now specialized and that the generalized forms on which major evolutionary developments depend are absent. In fact all animals have always been more or less specialized and a really generalized living form is merely a myth or an abstraction. It happens that there are still in existence some of the less specialized, that is, less narrowly adapted and more adaptable, forms from which radiations have occurred and could as far as we can see occur again. Opossums are not notably more specialized now than in the Cretaceous and could almost certainly radiate again markedly if available spaces were to occur again. Even primate re-radiation would be entirely possible if present primates were wiped out and their empty ecological niches continued to exist, because living tree shrews have no specializations that would clearly exclude approximate repetition of such a radiation. Of course such re-radiation could not be identical with or even closely similar to the radiations that have already occurred in the same groups, because close repetition of the same conditions is impossible. It is also extremely improbable that re-radiation will occur, simply because the results of earlier radiation are there, holding their ground; but the possibility certainly is not excluded. More likely, in view of the past record, would be either replacement or radiation of quite a new and unpredictable sort— unpredictable because we probably do not know enough to see the possibility. (Such possibilities can be imagined, although hardly predicted; for instance there are no truly aerial flora and fauna of organisms living and reproducing in air as a medium as seaweeds and fishes do in water, and there seems to be nothing downright impossible in such a development.)

If man were wiped out, it is extremely improbable that anything very similar to him would ever again evolve, although I cannot see that even this is altogether impossible. The exact ancestral forms are gone. The whole intricate sequence of biological and physical conditions that gave rise to man certainly will not be repeated with very close approximation. Yet it remains true that manlike intelligence and individual adaptability have high selective value in evolution and that other animals have a conceivable basis for similar development. One, at least, of its most ancient and fundamental requisites is actually quite common among mammals, even outside of the primates: use of the forefeet as hands for manipulation, with close hand-eye coordination, which is present not only in all primates but also in many rodents and some carnivores.

It is, however, reasonably safe to assume that no animals able to compete with man in intelligence, socialization, and the other unique human characteristics will arise as long as man does exist in fact. He has a firm grip on this adaptive zone and is fully able to defend it. The existence of man is a major element in defining and limiting possibilities of future evolution not only in this but also in practically all other respects. Man does broadly manipulate the environment and is learning how to do so more and more. He knows that evolution occurs and is fast learning exactly how it works. This must, if it continues, eventually make it possible for him to guide not only his own evolution but also that of any other organisms, if he so chooses. It is a decided possibility that he can really introduce finalism into organic evolution, which has conspicuously lacked a true goal in the past; the purpose and the end would, of course, be set and determined by man. He is rapidly coming to hold the power of life and death. He has casually caused the extinction of numerous other sorts of organisms and seems likely to devise means for causing extinction at will.

This awesome power includes the human prerogative of self-extinction. It is highly improbable that any organisms have ever become extinct as a result of their own activities alone and without some affliction unbidden and not determined wholly by their own natures. Man is probably quite capable of wiping himself out, or if he has not quite achieved the possibility as yet, he is making rapid progress in that direction.

If man does not exercise this, another of his unique capacities, or if in any case his extinction (ultimately inevitable) is long delayed, it is reasonably certain that he will evolve farther and will change more or less radically. It is hardly conceivable that even man's great powers will ever include the possibility of maintaining a frozen status quo in a changing universe. At present, in any case, cessation of human evolution is certainly not desirable or desired. By no standard of ethics whatever is human society now so good that any ethical man could wish it to persist unchanged or could fail to hope and to work for its improvement. On the biological side, few inhabitors of a human body can possibly think that it is perfect and that some change in it would not be highly desirable. Even those—movie stars, perhaps—who may think their own bodies incapable of improvement at the moment must deplore the approaching ravages of age and must, by the very contrast between themselves and others, perceive that the physical average for mankind needs changing. Whatever one may think of a possible future utopia in which man would be socially and biologically so perfect that any change would be for the worse, further human evolution now is obviously desirable provided, of course, that it is desirable in direction.

Man has the power to modify and within certain rather rigid limits to determine the direction of his own evolution. This power is increasing rapidly as knowledge of evolution increases. As regards biological evolution, this power has not as yet really been exercised systematically and consciously to any effective extent. Control of social evolution has also been much less in the past than it can be and is likely to be in the future, and has likewise been highly unsystematic and often not really conscious.

Invention by man of the new evolution, based on the inheritance of learning and worked out in social structures, has not eliminated in him the old organic evolution. The new evolution continues to interact with and in considerable measure to depend on the old. Guidance of the course of either will inevitably influence the other also, and can be most effective only by coordinated guidance of the two. This involves possible, although I think not necessary, conflict. Guidance of social evolution, to the extent that it is undertaken at all, necessarily follows some adopted ethical standards. That guidance becomes more difficult and its results slower if the ethical standards to be followed, like those discussed in the last chapter, hold that it is bad to impose regimentation or unnecessary compulsion on individuals.

The quickest and most effective guidance of biological evolution, too, could be achieved only by compulsion and therefore must here be held to be ethically bad. It is, nevertheless, possible for slower and less rigid but still, in the long run, effective guidance of both to be achieved in ways ethically good. It is each individual's responsibility to choose what he considers right directions for social and for biological evolution. With increase in knowledge and in its dissemination, there should eventually result sufficient unanimity on these points so that effective evolutionary motion would occur by voluntary individual actions. It is one of the known facts of organic evolution that a very minute incidence of natural selection will, under suitable circumstances, ultimately determine the direction of evolution. This involves the possibility that human evolution could be guided by united action of a small minority, although special conditions would be required for their action to become effective. It would, for instance, be ineffective if opposed by a different trend in the rest of the population, whether self-controlled or under the influence of natural selection only. It would be decisive if the direction of evolution were wholly random in the rest of the population or if it were about equally divided among different trends one of which coincided with that desired by the minority.

Under our ethics, the possibility of man's influencing the direction of his own evolution also involves his responsibility for doing so and for making that direction the best possible. Those ethics themselves define the best direction for social evolution. They also define in large measure the desirable directions for organic evolution, although the definition is indirect and less obvious.

The present organic structure of the human species is obviously consonant with far greater progress in the new evolution toward an ethical social ideal than has yet been achieved. Approach toward such an ideal must, however, also involve some physical evolutionary changes. Men differ greatly in intelligence, in temperament, and in various abilities that are in part, at least, hereditary. In some respects these differences are socially and ethically desirable. Differences in temperament are certainly desirable except for the relatively few temperaments that are incompatible with socially normal living. The good society would involve opportunities for the fullest development of every ethically good variety of temperament. Some differences in degree of intelligence may be desirable, but the point is debatable and in any case the raising of the average nearer to the present maximum is evidently desirable. Such changes as these would require provision of optimum environmental conditions, but could not be achieved by this means alone; genetic selection in the existing variability of the species would also be required. There is ample evidence that intelligence is if not strictly determined at least strictly limited as to potentialities by inheritance. Even temperament is apparently to some degree hereditary and correlated with physical structure, better knowledge of which would facilitate selection.[2]

Such changes, involving differences in distribution of existing characters within the human population, are evolutionary but they are of limited scope. Ultimate progress beyond these limits would necessarily involve the development of

[2] See, for instance, W. H. Sheldon, *The Varieties of Temperament* (New York and London, Harper, 1942). The evidence seems at present to be inconclusive and attempts to apply this knowledge now would be premature, but it does strongly suggest a future possibility.

new characters in the human organism. Probably the new character most surely necessary for evolution beyond the present limits is an increase in intelligence above the existing maximum. Human progress depends on knowledge and learning, and the capacity for these is conditioned by intelligence. Most scientists are already aware that the progress of science is being impeded by the fact that the most brilliant men simply do not have enough learning capacity to acquire all the details of more than increasingly narrow segments of the field of knowledge. Only a very stupid person can believe that mankind is already intelligent enough for its own good.

If and as it is achieved, this increase in intelligence will have other concomitants, among them a larger brain and changes to accommodate this, probably in the direction of making the adult more childlike in proportions.[3] Increase in length of life, besides corresponding with a nearly universal human desire, will also ultimately be necessary for intellectual and social progress, in order to allow for a longer juvenile learning period without subtracting from the period of adult life.

Many progressive changes which in other organisms would have to be physical, do not seem necessary or even desirable in man because they correspond with needs that he can supply more effectively and rapidly by technological means. There is no possible substitute for intelligence, but it can be greatly aided and supplemented. Organic development of new perceptual or, at least, sensory apparatus does not seem to be required for future human evolution. I am personally skeptical as to whether extrasensory perception, the other so-called psi phenomena, "group consciousness," and other such things dear to the hearts of many writers on the present and future of man really exist. Even if they do there is no reason to develop them because, as far as they might have any use, the same results can be achieved more fully and surely by mechanical means. It is, indeed, quite possible that development of such supposed phenomena would impede ethical progress.

The means of achieving biological evolutionary progress are already becoming clear, although it is doubtful whether we are yet ready to apply them well. The known avenues of such change are by environmental conditions of development, by selection, and by mutation (followed, of course, by selection). Control of environmental conditions is the only means

[3] It is well known that man today resembles the young more than the adults of other higher primates. On this and other points pertinent to the present chapter, see Haldane's provocative chapter, "Human Evolution: Past and Future," in *Genetics, Paleontology, and Evolution* (Princeton, Princeton University Press, 1949), edited by G. L. Jepsen, E. Mayr, and G. G. Simpson.

now commonly in use and it is definitely advancing, although much remains to be done. It permits exploration of the full potentialities of the human organism in the way of healthier bodies, realization of more nearly the full life span, and so on, but it does not change those potentialities.[4]

Further steps, if and when taken, must involve selection, that is, some degree of control over differential reproduction. In principle this could be completely controlled by man, but even partially effective control is almost impossible in the present state of society and it is doubtful whether really full control could ever be exercised in an ethically good social system. The right to apply it must be voluntarily granted by the individuals concerned. Its effectiveness and the determination of the right direction in which to apply it will demand a great deal of knowledge that we do not now possess. Eugenics has deservedly been given a bad name by many sober students in recent years because of the prematurity of some eugenical claims and the stupidity of some of the postulates and enthusiasms of what had nearly become a cult. We are also still far too familiar with some of the supposedly eugenical practices of the Nazis and their like. The assumption that biological superiority is correlated with color of skin, with religious belief, with social status, or with success in business is imbecile in theory and vicious in practice. The almost equally naïve, but less stupid and not especially vicious, idea that prevention of reproduction among persons with particular undesirable traits would quickly eradicate these traits in the population has also proved to be unfounded. The incidence of a few clearly harmful hereditary defects could be reduced by sterilization of the individuals possessing them, but they could not be wholly eliminated and in the light of present knowledge it is highly doubtful whether this means can produce any really noteworthy physical improvement in the human species as a whole.

Selection was, nevertheless, the means by which man arose and it is the means by which, if by any, his further organic evolution must be controlled. Man has so largely modified the impact of the sort of natural selection which produced him that desirable biological progression on this basis is not to be expected. There is no reason to believe that individuals with more desirable genetic characteristics now have more children than do those whose genetic factors are undesirable, and there is some reason to suspect the opposite. The present influence of natural selection on man is at least as likely to

---

[4] "Control of environmental conditions" of course includes prevention and cure of internal diseases, proper diet, and other factors of health, as well as full and proper development of the mind and of social relationships.

be retrogressive as progressive. Maintenance of something near the present biological level is probably about the best to be hoped for on this basis. The only proper possibility of progress seems to be in voluntary, positive social selection to produce in offspring new and improved genetic systems and to balance differential reproduction in favor of those having desirable genes and systems. As soon as we know what the desirable human genes and systems are and how to recognize them! The knowledge is now almost wholly lacking, but it seems practically certain that it is obtainable.

One thing that is definitely known now is that breeding for uniformity of type and for elimination of variability in the human species would be ethically, socially, and genetically bad and would not promote desirable evolution. This variability, with accompanying flexibility and capacity for individualization, is in itself ethically good, socially valuable, and evolutionarily desirable. Progress is impossible without change, and change is impossible without variation. We can therefore expect neither biological nor social progress unless we tolerate human differences both in physical type and in social ideas.

It happens that the present human breeding structure is excellent for the promotion of adaptability and desirable variability and for control of evolution by selection. The theoretically ideal conditions in this respect involve a large population with wide genetic variety (reflected also in local polymorphism), divided into many relatively small, habitually interbreeding groups which are not, however, completely isolated but also have some gene interchange between them. This ideal is actually rather closely approached in the present breeding structure of the human species. Its continuance as a basis for effective selection and maintenance of desirable variability demands avoidance of both of two extremes. On one hand, a completely classless society or habitual general intermingling in marriage of all racial or other groups would be bad, from this point of view. On the other hand, effective segregation and prohibition of interbreeding between any two or more racial, religious, or other groups would be even worse.

Selection can in the long run make the most of the genetic factors now existing in the human species. Eventually its possibilities would be exhausted if there were not also new mutations. Mutations are known to occur in mankind at rates comparable to those in other animals and consistent with sustained evolution at moderate speed. Almost all of those known are disadvantageous and produce abnormalities definitely undesirable in present society and probably of no value for any desirable future development. We probably completely miss in study of human heredity the very small favorable mutations that are likely to exist and to be more frequent than these larger and generally unfavorable mutations. The ability to recognize these small mutations will be a necessary factor if man is to advance his own biological evolution by voluntary selection. At present we do not have the slightest idea of how to produce to order the sort of mutation that may be needed or desired. We do not even know whether this is physically possible. If it is, and if man does discover the secret, then indeed evolution will pass fully into his control.

Now we cannot predict for sure whether the future course of human evolution will be upward or downward. We have, however, established the fact that it *can* be upward and we have a glimpse, although very far from full understanding, as to how to ensure this. It is our responsibility and that of our descendants to ensure that the future of the species is progressive and not retrogressive. The immediate tasks are to work for continuance of our species, for avoiding early self-extinction, settling ideological battles, and progressing toward an ethically good world state. The immediate means not only for these tremendous tasks but also for the future task of guiding human evolution lie within the ethic of knowledge. We need desperately to know more about ourselves, about our societies, about all of life, about the earth, and about the universe. We need to balance our knowledge better, to reverse the disparity in discovery in the physical, biological, and social sciences so that the social sciences shall be first and the physical last. We need to realize more fully and widely that technological advances and the invention and enjoyment of gadgets are not the most useful sort of knowledge and are relatively quite unimportant (occasionally downright harmful) for true human progress. We need to remember that cultural evolution proceeds only by interthinking, as organic evolution does only by interbreeding. The most brilliant of geniuses is an intellectual eunuch if his knowledge is not disseminated as widely as possible. It is immoral for any man, industry, or nation to reserve knowledge for its own advantage alone.

We need, too, to recognize the supreme importance of knowledge of organic and of social evolution. Such knowledge provides most of what we know of our place in the universe and it must guide us if we are to control the future evolution of mankind.

Epilogue

IT HAS been a long journey down the corridors of time to this point where mankind looks with foreboding and yet with hope into the mists of the future. We have followed a billion years of the history of life; we have examined some of the processes by which life has changed and developed; and we have come at the end to consideration of ourselves, the only form of life that knows it has a history, the thinking, responsible, and ethical animals.

Among the questions that have been discussed are some that everyone has asked, in one form or another, and for which everyone has had to find some sort of answer, whether vague or definite, unthinkingly accepted or carefully formulated. This is true because of the very fact that we are human beings and that it is a characteristic of humanity to be conscious of self, to have some sort of concept of what man is and some sort of judgment of his actions. There are many possibile approaches to the problems of existence and of values. All should be followed, for none can hope to achieve a total solution and each may be expected to illumine a different aspect of the riddle of human life. Here we have started with the premise that life has evolved and has had a history. This premise has been so conclusively established by generations of study and the resultant accumulation of literally millions of concordant facts that it has become almost self-evident and requires no further proof to anyone reasonably free of old illusions and prejudices.

This premise taken as established, an enquiry into the nature and meaning of life based on it seems, certainly not the only one possible or required, but the most direct and the most fundamental as basis for any further enquiry. This nature and this meaning must, if anywhere, be apparent in the history that has brought man and all other forms of life into being and in the processes of that history. The general outline of that history and some of its characteristic details are now so well determined as to provide a factual background open to little serious question. It is, however, still true that the unknown exceeds the known and gives room for some (yet for limited) differences of interpretation. And even were all factually known, which can never become true, interpretation would still be necessary before meaning could arise from the factual record. Differences of interpretation will no doubt always arise, and this or any other reading of meaning into the history of life can never carry compulsive authority. It can only be an opinion submitted for judgment and each of us is still required to exercise his responsibility to take nothing on faith but to make rational choice.

The existence of this personal responsibility for choice and decision is one of the conclusions of the present study, and it applies to the study itself and to the readers of it. Yet it would be improper to present this with undue humility. Any conclusions, certainly including those here reached, may be false as well as true and any may be responsibly rejected as well as accepted by those to whom they are presented. If, however, evidence is given for those conclusions and the ways of interpreting that evidence are set forth, no one can honestly turn to the conclusions and say, "This I will believe," or "That I refuse to believe," without some weighing of reasons and some positive knowledge to confirm his decisions.[1]

The history of life is to be studied by a great variety of means, among which special importance attaches to the actual historical record in rocks and the fossils contained in them. The rocks indicate that the earth, only home of life surely known to us, has existed in approximately its present form and with roughly the same physical surface conditions for at least 2,000,000,000 years. Direct record of life extends back well over 1,000,000,000 years. The very beginnings of life are not known in the record and in the nature of things could not be adequately recorded, if at all. Studies on other bases demonstrate not only the possibility but also the probability that life arose from the inorganic spontaneously, that is, without supernatural intervention and by the operation of material processes, themselves of unknown origin, sometime during the first half billion years or so of the earth's existence in about its present condition. After long obscurity during which the basic complexity of cellular organization was developed, there came a time, extending over several millions of years, during which fundamental divergence produced most of the broadest structural and functional types of living organisms that were ever to exist. This occurred around 500,000,000 years ago, and since that time life has left a continuous and fairly full record of its own history.

[1] Human nature being what it is, there will surely be some who turn first to these concluding remarks in the hope of learning what this book may have to offer without plowing through the preceding discussion. It would be most humorless arrogance to attempt to order them to turn back to page one, but they should be told that one of the conclusions is that there is no ethical right to judge without consideration of the basis for judgment.

Few, if any, of the broadest and most basic types have ever become extinct. The more complex and, in some sense, higher types have in some cases changed greatly and on the whole have changed more than the lower types. All main types represent abilities to follow broadly distinctive ways of life, and the earlier or lower persist along with the later and higher because these latter represent not competitors doing the same sorts of things as their lower ancestors but groups developing distinctly new ways of life. Each main group shows, in the record, at least one period of major expansion when it was (or is) particularly abundant and varied. Expansion and contraction in different groups follow highly diverse ways and there is no suggestion of a standard pattern or over-all plan. The sum of all these effects, the total number and variety of organisms existing in the world, has shown a tendency to increase markedly during the history of life, but even this has shown much inconstancy and fluctuation.

Expansions of a given group commonly occur by radiation into a variety of related ways of life. When groups living under quite different conditions and with unrelated ways of life expand in this way, there is no evident tendency for their expansions either to coincide or to be successive. Within any one general way of life there is a tendency for successive expansions, each to some extent replacing the last but often not completely eradicating it. Among land vertebrates, with broadly related ways of life, there have been successive expansions of amphibians, reptiles, and mammals. Primates arose in the main mammalian radiation and had themselves, within the group, a succession of radiations partly replacing older groups and partly extending into new ways of life. Man arose from the most recent of these primate radiations.

In attempting to interpret this history the major problem, both philosophical and scientific, is to decide whether it has taken place under the action of universal and natural principles, and so is materialistic; whether it has involved principles new in and peculiar to life, making it vitalistic; and whether, in either case, it does or does not represent the working out of some supernal purpose, involving an over-all plan and progressing toward a goal, the finalistic interpretation.

Examined in more detail, the history of life turns out to be an odd and intricate mixture of the oriented and the random. Continuing and clearly oriented trends of evolutionary change are very common, but when carefully studied without gross oversimplification, they give no appearance of rigid control forcing them in only one direction. They also lack evidence of any vital inner force or momentum that carries them forward regardless of the functional adaptation to way of life or of any random change. The evidence all concurs in suggesting that the orienting force in evolution is neither internal nor external to the organisms involved but is in that interplay of both internal and external factors which produces adaptation to way of life and to environment.

Evolution appears to be not only a mixture of random and of oriented changes but also highly opportunistic, in a purely impersonal sense. Most, although not all, of the possible ways of life in any given period of earth history have usually been followed by one group or another. Among possible different solutions of a given functional problem, such as that of perception of light, many or all are commonly followed by various groups. There is no effect of over-all plan tending toward the same solution of such a problem. Solutions are not achieved in the way theoretically best but on the basis of what happens to be available, apparently by chance. Patterns of racial life and death, of survival and extinction, expansion and contraction, are also extremely varied and are opportunistic, correlated with the possibilities of existing physical factors, and not with any conceivable over-all plan or ultimate purpose.

Although many details remain to be worked out, it is already evident that all the objective phenomena of the history of life can be explained by purely materialistic factors. They are readily explicable on the basis of differential reproduction in populations (the main factor in the modern conception of natural selection) and of the mainly random interplay of the known processes of heredity. Vitalist and finalist theories not only fail to explain them but are also flatly inconsistent with them. These theories are commonly not truly explanatory but are frequently more or less veiled attempts to evade explanation. They arose in part as efforts to salvage unscientific prejudices really contradicted by the facts of evolution, but some were also legitimate reactions to the fact that proposed materialistic explanations were long unsatisfactory and that the effort to complete them was in a temporary impasse. Discovery of the facts of genetics and integration of these with knowledge of life from other fields of study have led out of this impasse and produced a materialistic theory that no longer gives motive for vitalistic or finalistic evasions.

All-over progress, and particularly progress toward any goal or fixed point, can no longer be considered as characteristic of evolution or even as inherent in it. Progress does exist in the history of life, but it is of many different sorts and each sort occurs separately in many different lines. One sort of progress in structure and function that stands out as particularly widespread and important is increasing awareness of the life situation of the individual organism and increasing variety and sureness of appropriate reactions to this. Among the many different lines that show progress in this respect, the line leading to man reaches much the highest level yet developed. By most other criteria of progress, also, man is at least among the higher animals and a balance of considerations fully warrants considering him definitely the highest of all.

Man is the result of a purposeless and materialistic process that did not have him in mind. He was not planned. He is a state of matter, a form of life, a sort of animal, and a species of the Order Primates, akin nearly or remotely to all of life and indeed to all that is material. It is, however, a gross misrepresentation to say that he is *just* an accident or *nothing but* an animal. Among all the myriad forms of matter and of life on the earth, or as far as we know in the universe, man is unique. He happens to represent the highest form of organization of matter and energy that has ever appeared. Recognition of this kinship with the rest of the universe is necessary for understanding him, but his essential nature is defined by qualities found nowhere else, not by those he has in common with apes, fishes, trees, fire, or anything other than himself.

It is part of this unique status that in man a new form of evolution begins, overlying and largely dominating the old, organic evolution which nevertheless also continues in him. This new form of evolution works in the social structure, as the old evolution does in the breeding population structure, and it depends on learning, the inheritance of knowledge, as the old does on physical inheritance. Its possibility arises from man's intelligence and associated flexibility of response. His reactions depend far less than other organisms' on physically inherited factors, far more on learning and on perception of immediate and of new situations.

This flexibility brings with it the power and the need for constant choice between different courses of action. Man plans and has purposes. Plan, purpose, goal, all absent in evolution to this point, enter with the coming of man and are inherent in the new evolution, which is confined to him. With them comes the need for criteria of choice. Good and evil, right and wrong, concepts largely irrelevant in nature except from the human viewpoint, become real and pressing features of the whole cosmos as viewed by man—the only possible way in which the cosmos can be viewed morally because morals arise only in man.

Discovery that the universe apart from man or before his coming lacks and lacked any purpose or plan has the inevitable corollary that the workings of the universe cannot provide any automatic, universal, eternal, or absolute ethical criteria of right and wrong. This discovery has completely undermined all older attempts to find an intuitive ethic or to accept such an ethic as revelation. It has not been so generally recognized that it equally undermines attempts to find a naturalistic ethic which will flow with absolute validity from the workings of Nature or of Evolution as a new Revelation. Such attempts, arising from discovery of the baselessness of intuitive ethics, have commonly fallen into the same mistake of seeking an absolute ethic or one outside of man's own nature and have then been doomed to failure by their own premises.

The ethical need is within and peculiar to man, and its fulfillment also lies in man's nature, relative to him and to his evolution, not external or unchanging. Man has choice and responsibility, and in this matter, too, he must choose and he cannot place responsibility for rightness and wrongness on God or on nature. The choices here proposed and placed before the reader for his acceptance or rejection in accordance with his own responsibility are, first, based on the proposition that knowledge is good and, second, derived from the substantially proven fact that man does possess personal responsibility. In all, these ethics flow from the unique qualities of man and from what is conceived to be his real place in nature.

The fact of responsibility and the ethic of knowledge have many ethical corollaries, among them that blind faith ("blind," or "unreasoning," to be emphasized) is morally wrong. In connection with high individualization, another human diagnostic character, the resulting ethics include the goodness of maintenance of this individualization and promotion of the integrity and dignity of the individual. Socialization, a necessary human process, may be good or bad. When ethically good, it is based on and in turn gives maximum *total* possibility for ethically good individualization.

Such ethics have wide applications in social and personal conduct. They stand in strong opposition to authoritarian or totalitarian ideologies. They confirm the existence of many evils in current democracies, but the good state, on these principles, would inevitably be a democracy. The principles do not label every human action as good or bad—to do this would violate the prior conclusion that valid ethics cannot be absolute. Moreover, individual variability and flexibility are in themselves desirable, from the point of view both of ethics and of evolution, biological and social.

Beyond the subjects of this enquiry are mysteries deeper still, unplumbed by paleontology or any other science. The boundaries of what can be achieved by perception and by reason are respected. The present chaotic stage of humanity is not, as some wishfully maintain, caused by lack of faith but by too much unreasoning faith and too many conflicting faiths within these boundaries where such faith should have no place. The chaos is one that only responsible human knowledge can reduce to order.

It is another unique quality of man that he, for the first time in the history of life, has increasing power to choose his course and to influence his own future evolution. The possibility of choice can be shown to exist. This makes rational the hope that choice may sometime lead to what is good and right for man. Responsibility for defining and for seeking that end belongs to all of us.

Index

Asterisks denote illustrations